First edition published August 2010 by
Colosseum Publishing
2400 Kettner Blvd. Suite F-109
San Diego, CA 92101
Publishing@ColosseumFineArts.com

ISBN 978-0-9828407-0-2

Printed in The United States of America

For my family and Amanda

To Katie

And Sean, Len, Koss, Jim, Jerry Bob, Jaime, Mike, Matt, Quintin, Kimble, Evan, the Firm, Tom Yazvac, Edie, Bob, Jules, the CityBusiness crew, Jazzy, Danny, Aisha, Ruby, Grace, and Lil' Axl.

CONTENTS

DISCLAIMER:

Bubbles from Atlantis includes bylined articles written by the author and republished with the permission of New Orleans CityBusiness. It also includes mindless rants and stream-of-consciousness observations created while under the influence of booze, chemicals, rage, depression, paranoia, and an undying love for New Orleans. Portions of the content of these aforementioned rants and observations have been embellished, exaggerated, and fabricated to support a larger and more disturbing message. As previously stated, the author has serious mental issues and much of this book is a product of his psychosis. May God bless the poor bastard's soul.

BUBBLES FROM ATLANTIS

By Richard A. Webster

Art by Sean Dietrich

First Entry: Oct 23, 2005
The Proclamation

"THE GREAT HOPE RIGHT NOW,
THE DREAM THAT MARCHES ON OUR
SENSES,
THAT BOILS THE BITTER FUEL OF OUR HEARTS,
IS THAT THE POPULACE WILL RISE UP."

I'm fucked-up.

Let me make that much clear.

But that doesn't make me original or unique.

It makes me one of several hundred thousand fucked-up survivors trying to make a go of it in this, the post-massacre land known to the world as New Orleans.

We're all fucked-up.

You would be too.

Trust me.

On this subject, I know what the hell I'm talking about.

And soon, you will too.

I'm going to let you in on the secret.

I'm going to fill your head with visions of Visigoths storming baby cradles with bureau-cratic bloodlust, hydro-powered sadists rushing through the doors of once happy homes, or the semblance of once happy homes, with crossbred intentions that would make Pi-nochet piss his pants.

The storm was bad. But she couldn't hold a goddamn candle compared to what we're fac-ing in these post-Katrina days.

The storm--the winds and rain and nasty descending darkness--she wasn't shit.

Poor Mother Nature, proud, vengeful, benevolent and beautiful Mother Nature, she did her best to show us all how small we are. She howled and ripped tits and made helpless children cry. Shit, she made grown men cry, the macho tribe of gun-blazing bison who hump tree trunks just to prove they can produce bark babies if the mood struck them.

It's not my intention to diminish the power of Mother Nature. She's got the winning lot-tery ticket. If she chose to cash it in I'd be writing this rant from a shack in the far corners of limbo. Or working it out in my froggy reincarnated head, hopping to and fro among the lily pad rooftops of the long lost city of New Orleans, desperately attempting to flick my tongue across my back with the hope that I am one of those psychotropic toadies red-necks get high off of when the meth lab runs dry.

But despite the apocalyptic weather forecasts leading up to Katrina's landfall, Mother Nature took it easy on us. The storm of all storms hit New Orleans as a Category 3.

Telephone poles timbered, houses caved under a cascade of collapsing trees and windows exploded in glorious flashes of glittery glass. But we survived, for the most part, here in New Orleans.

The storm passed, the sun burst through clouds, birds chirped those old bluegrass tunes, and heads popped out of barricaded homes, surveying the damage, acknowledging familiar heads down the street extended out of chimneys, whispering tender blessings and blessing tender angels for granting us yet another reprieve.

And in the far-flung reaches of the states, evacuees rejoiced as cable news carried word of the triumph of New Orleans.

Another near miss.

Pack your bags momma. It's happy hour on Decatur Street. The Big Easy is alive and well.

And then the levees gave way.

And we all know what happened next.

I'm fucked-up.

Let me make that much clear.

But that doesn't make me original or unique.

It makes me one of several hundred thousand fucked-up survivors trying to make a go of it in this, the post-massacre land known to the world as New Orleans.

I'm also drifting into serial alcoholism.

That doesn't make me unique either.

It didn't make me unique before the storm and it doesn't make me unique after.

And as a journalist, it makes me a cliché.

We writers, as a general rule, we're all holy-rolling lushes, wet-heads working out our demons on keyboard and page, doing our best to stave off suicide and salvation.

Sometimes it's hard to tell the difference between the two, especially in these post-storm days of death and damnation.

But goddammit, I'm after something more.

I'm not ready for suicide, not just yet.

And I don't think salvation is within reach, not just yet.

Or damnation for that matter.

What I want, what I demand, is some accountability, some recognition, not for myself, but for my city and my people.

Before y'all stick a tombstone in the ground for New Orleans, before you genuflect before our swampy souls, I request a one-on-one with your God.

I got a couple of things I need to get off my chest.

I'll even wear a tie if it makes a difference.

I'll comb my hair and iron my shirt.

I'll tell the demons entrenched on my crooked shoulders to shut their precious mouths.

But what I won't do is hold my tongue.

In my hands I hold a proclamation I intend to nail into the foreheads of every priest and politician and pundit within reach of my hammer.

And I intend to drive the nail deep enough to make an impression.

You dig?

I'm fucked-up and drunk and with the passing of each day my rage expands.

I'm trapped in a dying city populated by the best of the rest, doing my best to hold it together long enough to document what I fear could be the last gasps of my own personal Eden. By day I interview the broken and determined, the tribal members, strong and weak, some brandishing cleavers at the sun, others trembling in the shadows, chewing on heroin fig leaves.

I piece together their words into semi-literate articles published for the consumption of whoever, in the great expanse of America, chooses to give a damn about our fate. And by night I get loose with a shotgun, a 12-pack of Budweiser and a bottle of pills, dragging my brain along a barbed-wire fence for wordy inspiration, spewing and spilling my guts and bile onto page so I don't choke to death in my sleep.

Straight journalism by day, booze-soaked ranting by night.

These are the weapons at my disposal and I intend to use them to lay waste to the hypocrites condemning the people of New Orleans by day, pawing at their stepdaughters' doors by night.

I intend to use them to lay hands on the voluntarily blind who refuse to accept what is happening to us, to my beloved, troubled city, a boiling Sanitarium by day, a blackout suicide ward by night.

And I intend to use them to lay to rest in shallow graves dug out of our watery soil, the purposefully ignorant, the joyfully stupid fuckers who just don't give a shit one way or another.

But above all, I intend to use these weapons of mine to lay down our story, to etch these stick figure nightmares into the base of your skull, so when we're long gone, victims of vice, perpetrators of our own demise, survivors of the federal plague, you won't soon forget the woeful, fucked-up tale of the people of New Orleans.

Tormented, mind-wrecked, noble lovers by day.

Tormented, mind-wrecked, noble lovers by night.

We're consistent if nothing else.

And So it Begins

Oh fragile time you whip me like a slave.

For those of you who had the good fortune to visit the old New Orleans before it succumbed to the promise of the gills, cradle those liver scars you earned in our bars and lovingly caress them at night once your lover has passed out under the creeping influence of forever and regret.

The old New Orleans is dead.

She don't live here no more.

14

Our once proud populace has shrunk from just under 500,000 to approximately 50,000, give or take a Red Cross volunteer, National Guard contingent or Hispanic migrant laborer.

The populated area is a fine slip of land running from Uptown through the Central Business District to the French Quarter and ending in the Bywater/Faubourg Marigny neighborhood.

We the people of the 24-hour bar operate under a 2 a.m. curfew, 8 p.m. in those areas still dark and mostly free of human life.

Once the clock hits 2 a.m. scores of pimply-faced National Guardsmen flow through the bar doors, M-16s slung around their backs.

Time to go home.

Most stores and services are shuttered by 6 p.m. Forget to hit the grocery store beforehand, you're fucked unless you want to wait for two hours at one of the joints on the growing list of restaurants open for business.

The sidewalks and neutral grounds are packed and stacked high with duct-taped refrigerators, the new Fleur de Lis, the unofficial symbol of New Orleans--self-contained toxic waste containers fat with maggot-shaped bacteria and grey hairy mounds of meat, gently throbbing with each threatening breath.

They are legion.

And oh that smell my brothers and sisters--it does rip the membrane from your nasal passages.

And with these godforsaken refrigerators, the piles of black garbage bags amassing on the sidewalks and the stinking, filthy dumpsters, come the swarms--fruit flies and sand flies with fluorescent green eyes and yet-to-be identified insects that pile on with no sense of fair play.

Doron, an Israeli jeweler/writer from Pittsburgh, walked into the Avenue Pub nine days ago.

"You staying?" he asked.

"Hell yes."

"Shit. You're a better man than I am," Doron said. "I'm getting my shit and going back to Pittsburgh. This place creeps me out."

And so it goes.

Out with the blacks and in with the Latino construction workers. They gather at the Shell station blocks from my house in their cowboy boots and hats, swilling paper bag beers while waiting in line to use the pay phone.

They earn more than $10 an hour working 12-hour shifts, sending cash home or down the g-strings of strippers overworked by FEMA fed-er-ah-leees and other D.C. chumps getting their bureaucratic rocks off.

There's no such thing as a minimum wage in New Orleans. It's a relic of a long-gone time. Burger King offers a $6,000 bonus and starting pay of $10 or more to sling cow fat. Waitresses and bartenders pull in $500 a night.

We drink and we eat, desperate for company and the ability to forget just how fucked it all is.

It is a childless city. Anything under 17 years is a mutant or a mirage. We have no schools and few hospitals. Small, clear bottles of hand sanitizer are a fashionable accessory.

It is a city free of the homeless, all washed away or bused to Texas, except for a handful of true survivors like Betty on the corner of Canal and Broad. Members of Unity of Greater New Orleans, a local homeless advocacy group, tried to get her out of town before the storm but she refused. They gave her up for dead. What hope did she have? But when they returned, amid the wreckage and bodies, there was Betty, on her corner, telling the world to go fuck itself.

Turns out guards at Orleans Parish Prison took her in. Sort of ruins the miracle, but this ain't no fairy tale.

* * * * * * * * * *

NO loses 10,000 homeless people to uncertain fates
By Richard A. Webster New Orleans CityBusiness Staff Writer

October 10, 2005 -- With a Category 5 monster hurricane named Katrina churning up destruction in the Gulf of Mexico, Vicki Judice, director of public policy for Unity of Greater New Orleans, begged a homeless woman who lives at the intersection of Canal and Broad streets, known only as "Betty," to go to one of the local shelters.

"She looked me in the eyes and said, 'I've been through plenty of storms baby and I'm gonna make it through this one,'" Judice said.

After Katrina made landfall and the devastation of New Orleans became apparent, Judice and Unity Executive Director Martha Kegel quietly mourned the apparent death of Betty, who had become a colorful fixture in the community.

"We were sure she had passed away because that area took on a lot of water," Kegel said. "But last Friday when we drove into New Orleans to get some equipment and records from our office, I was astounded because who was sitting on this completely desolate corner that looks like Mars but (Betty)."

Kegel jumped out of the car, ran up to Betty and told her how happy she was to see her alive.

"She was sitting there rocking back and forth saying, 'There's no place like home, there's no place like home,' with this big smile on her face," Kegel said. "I tried to hug her and

she recoiled and said, 'Don't get sentimental on me.' She's a testament to the resilience of homeless people."

Though Betty survived Katrina, the fate of approximately 10,000 homeless people who once lived in New Orleans is more uncertain.

Kegel believes the majority of the homeless were evacuated through the Superdome or by service agencies. There is no way yet to tell how many of the approximately 1,150 chronically homeless remained during the storm and how many died during its aftermath.

"There may be more people than we thought who stayed behind. I think a large percentage was evacuated. We believe others perished," Kegel said.

Unity is tracking down clients who did evacuate. New Orleans Mission counselor Rusty Wirth is searching every shelter in Baton Rouge and Hammond looking for familiar faces.

"We want to make sure that homeless people are getting the same services as everybody else, things like FEMA assistance," said Wirth.

Wirth believes a large percentage of the homeless may not return to New Orleans.

"I think what will happen is if they get services and get settled and if it looks like they'll get some opportunities they'll stay where they're at," he said.

That won't end homelessness in the Crescent City though.

"I think we'll have a new wave of homelessness come in. The hurricane didn't instantly solve the problem of homelessness in New Orleans. As soon as the city is back up and running there will be homelessness again. That's just a fact of life," said Wirth.

Kegel agrees that many of the homeless will not return but it is important to provide for those who do.

"There has to be a meaningful 'right to return' for anyone living in New Orleans who wants to return," Kegel said. "There has to be government support to provide for bus fare and affordable housing once they get here. New Orleans won't be New Orleans if the only people here are wealthy people. If lower-income people aren't provided with a way to get back we'll lose the soul of New Orleans."

The thousands of homeless people from New Orleans spread out in neighboring communities, however, are straining the local social service agencies.

"We're getting word from Shreveport and Monroe that they're being inundated with new and old homeless," Judice said. "And the people being left at their shelters are the ones with all the disabilities, mental illness and substance abuse problems, people you just can't throw FEMA money at or rental assistance because they need more support than that. That's the reality. Everyone else is now having to deal with our former homeless."

Terri Brock, executive director of Hope for the Homeless in Shreveport, said the 55 agencies she oversees in a nine-parish region serve up to 1,300 homeless individuals every day.

After Hurricane Katrina, that number tripled to nearly 4,000.

"I had a national Red Cross person in here who has been through 16 national disasters in 20 years and he said he has never experienced anything like this," Brock said.

Shreveport typically has a homeless population of 4,500 but that number is expected to swell as nearly 2,500 homeless people from New Orleans plan to stay, according to Hope for the Homeless.

Many of the post-storm homeless lived in apartments or houses before Katrina, Brock said. But they lost their jobs and the apartments or houses they rented. They had no renter's insurance, savings or retirement fund.

Kegel said it is essential that in rebuilding New Orleans people take the homeless and less fortunate into account.

"The best way we can memorialize the people who needlessly died in Katrina is to make the city more sensitive to the plight of people in poverty and more helpful to those trying to pull themselves out of poverty," Kegel said.

* * * * * * * * * *

Poverty.

That is New Orleans.

Brain-strangling poverty.

But you don't run into many of the poor these days.

The housing projects are barren and abandoned and bombed out. Down Martin Luther King Jr. Boulevard, near the B.W. Cooper Housing Development, scores of cars and hearses and stolen limos and milk trucks crowd the sidewalks and neutral grounds, relics from the days of chaos.

But it's all quiet now except for the Chinooks, Humvees and other military monsters that patrol our streets and skies, though their numbers are fast dwindling. And that doesn't sit well with the small pack of people living in New Orleans, rubbing sticks together in a futile gambit to restart civilization.

Despite our anti-establishment attitude the boys in camouflage are our friends. They are the wall between us and the crooked fucking cops with their gravy-stained holsters.

Johnny Hollywood from New Jersey moved back into my Central City building five days ago.

"I had a friend who lives in the Bywater and he stayed throughout the storm," Hollywood said. "A few weeks ago he was returning home from work. It was after curfew and the cops stopped him and asked what he was doing. He said that he just got off from work and was walking home. One of the cops punched him square in the jaw. Broke it. The other two cops threw him on the ground and beat him. They took off his glasses and stepped on them. Then they sent him off into the night. He didn't leave his apartment for two days."

An EMT named Karley who drinks at the Avenue spun her own tale of cop horror. Her crew of EMTs waited out the storm at the Riverwalk mall with the 3rd District police. After the storm, when civil unrest hit its peak, she said the cops began to loot the joint, piling their treasure into their squad cars before hitting the road. The EMTs pounded on the cop windows begging to be taken to safety but the police said they had no more room in their cars and blew dust.

"They looked us in the eyes and said, 'You're on your own,'" Karley said.

What the world saw on October 9, 2005--two NOPD cops beating 64-year old Robert Davis, a retired school teacher on Bourbon Street, while a third bitch-slapped an AP reporter--is business as usual in post-Katrina New Orleans.

They said he was drunk.

He said he hasn't had a drink in 25 years.

They said he resisted arrest.

He said, "Hell yes," he resisted arrest.

What would you do if a mob of cops was stomping you into the ground for no damn good reason?

Do your civic duty and take it like a chump?

I'm not saying that there aren't good, heroic cops who risked their lives during Katrina and who deserve all of our prayers and positive thoughts, but a Letter to the Editor in the Times Picayune summed it up.

It was from a white man, a middle class white man with a family who wrote to say he was getting the fuck out of dodge.

It went something like this.

"I'm not afraid of the thugs or the criminal element," he wrote. "I'm afraid of the cops. And it was the same before the storm. So I'm packing up my belongings and moving to a city where the police don't play games with expandable batons, mace and animal knuckles. Good luck to the brave who choose to stay. I'm outta here."

He's outta here and the rest of the country is moving on.

New Orleans be boring.

Hurricane, flood, screaming babies, blah, blah, blah....

At a press conference I attended last week, Mayor C. Ray Nagin said it best. "I just got back from Washington and when I looked into the eyes of Congress I didn't like what I saw. We're on our own."

That's the prevailing consensus. After the emotion of seeing dead bodies on TV and people screaming for help outside the Superdome and Convention Center, the good feelings and intentions have expired.

Memo to New Orleans: Fuck you.

Yeah, we're good and fucked. But for we who live in those areas largely left intact by Katrina, it's easy to forget how truly fucked we are. Bars and restaurants have reopened. It's slowly back to business as usual. But take a trip outside our little slip of land, to the lower Ninth Ward or Lakeview or Mid-City or Chalmette and you'll witness devastation beyond all comprehension.

Cars on houses, houses lifted by the flood waters, turned around and dropped back down, the front door now the back door, and houses that are simply gone, not destroyed, but missing altogether.

A woman trapped in the attic of her Ninth Ward home for two weeks described seeing an alligator attack and kill her uncle. The Ninth Ward is an inner-city neighborhood. There aren't supposed to be fucking gators floating on bloated bellies snapping old black men in half.

And then there are the stories of small bull sharks, three to four feet, also seen swimming in the Ninth Ward. Stories that would seem easy to dismiss until you talk to fishermen who said it is completely possible for these sharks, adaptable to freshwater, to move through the hole in the levee for some urban orgiastic hi-jinks.

If someone from the Ninth told me they saw a harem of mermaids tear a whale apart with chainsaws, I'd believe it.

We're on an island in a largely dead city. But we're doing our best. Unfortunately, our best needs federal assistance, that graciously promised largesse that has yet to materialize. As small business owners reopen, their landlords demand rent they are unable to make. The Small Business Administration has promised loans but they won't come for months by which time these shops will be out of business.

As I said, we're doing our best to bounce back and be positive but it's my belief that we are in the lull before another storm of economic ruin. It's an awful prediction to make and I hope I'm wrong.

In the meantime, we gather at night in bars with recently reconnected friends to re-solidify bonds momentarily severed. It was only a few months ago that we were all together, but those two months apart felt like years spent in the lobby of a funeral parlor staring at the portraits of a massacre. So when we get together now, it's as if the alien ship landed and spit out all your loved ones, frozen in time, eyes foggy, not quite understanding what in the hell just happened.

Shell-shocked victims wandering out of the jungle clutching bottles of rum purchased on Aug. 28, carefully watching the horizon for flying cars shooting laser beams at talking apes. But who knows? Maybe it will all work out. But if it does, whatever IT is, it will be nothing like what any of you who once visited our besotted world remember.

20

Cooter Brown is reopened in a triumph over looters
By Richard A. Webster New Orleans CityBusiness Staff Writer

October 10, 2005 -- After 32 chaotic days of desolation and darkness, clashes with armed gangs of looters and long hours spent repairing damage from the bruising blows of Hurricane Katrina, Art Depodesta reopened his restaurant at Cooter Brown's on Thursday evening.

Paul Cosma, owner of the neighboring Uptown Auto Specialists, said despite New Orleans' "ghost town" status business at Cooter Brown's has been brisk.

"All the SWAT guys and cops from out of town are coming in," Cosma said. "Last night 30 of them came by in an hour. But who knows what's going to happen in the long run. It's the whole uncertainty of everything. None of us know what's going to happen."

Depodesta said all he can do is get his place up and running and hope for the best.

"The colleges are a big part of our business so without them it will definitely hurt," Depodesta said. "This was going to be a record year for us … but if we can hold out until after the first of the year business will pick up again."

Depodesta pays $30,000 a year for insurance and $5,500 a month in utilities, but he said it is the rising price of gas that has him most worried.

"Everything comes in by truck and if they have to pay more for gas the delivery prices go up which means I could have to jack the price of a burger up to $10 and if that happens no one gets paid," Depodesta said.

The structural damage to the Cooter Brown's building was limited though the roof peeled off directly above Depodesta's newly renovated second floor apartment. He and Cosma patched it up only to have Hurricane Rita undo all of their work.

The real damage occurred inside the restaurant's freezers, Cosma said.

"Can you imagine $20,000 worth of oysters, roasts, pastramis, hams, burgers, chickens and every kind of food you have at a restaurant like that? Can you imagine freezers full of this kind of food gone bad? It was pretty rude."

Depodesta and Cosma sprayed the freezers with bleach using a pump sprayer, then pressure washed them. After all of that work, two of the freezers blew up when the electricity returned.

Due to the loss of his freezers and a limited staff, Cosma said Depodesta will offer a limited menu.

"He'll be doing a limited menu only because many of his workers don't even have a place to live so he can't bring his whole crew in," Cosma said. "I loaned him my truck so he

can make food runs out to his suppliers in Harahan."

It has been hard work repairing and rebuilding his business but nothing compared to what took place in the aftermath of Katrina, said Depodesta.

The trouble started almost immediately after Katrina passed, even before the first levee broke.

After the heaviest winds died to a breeze, Depodesta and Cosma drove to the St. Charles Tavern on St. Charles Avenue - armed with guns to defend themselves.

"Paul had his Sig and I had my .45," Depodesta said. "We're all strapped up and the guys in the Tavern are handing us beers through the window. They had their weapons out, too."

And that's when Depodesta said he saw them — stolen cars tearing up and down St. Charles Avenue packed with masked men pointing guns at innocent people stumbling down sidewalks in search of information.

"Besides the flooding the biggest problem we had were these idiots after the storm," Depodesta said. "They were like animals. The cops are trying to rescue people and these idiots are going around shooting people. There aren't enough cops to begin with and they don't get paid anything anyway so they couldn't help. The one thing I learned was don't count on anyone but yourself. And never go to a shelter."

Depodesta and Cosma returned to their businesses and prepared for the worst. It wasn't long before gangs of thugs appeared on Carrollton Avenue.

"They started coming down the street and when they got close I let loose with a 12 gauge and they went running," Depodesta said. "One guy came back in a truck with a gun but we had the drop on him. I had a buddy here with an HK and I had my 12 gauge. When the guy in the truck saw that he decided he didn't want to play anymore. Let's just put it that way."

Things proceeded to get weirder, Depodesta said.

"They stole a damn forklift, drove it down to Rite Aid and lifted open the gates. Me and Paul went down there and cut all of the wires out of it. The last thing I want is a guy driving around here with a forklift."

A few days after the storm, Cosma grabbed a pair of bolt cutters from a suspected looter.

"First the kid said it was his uncle's, then he said he was going to come back and shoot us," Depodesta said. "I said, 'Go ahead man. It's like martial law. In fact there is no law so come on back here because I know damn well I'm a better shot than you and have better weapons.' I made it through the storm and had no flooding and then I got to watch some animals tear apart the place I built? I don't think so."

When the military arrived four days after Katrina made landfall, Depodesta said they attempted to confiscate his weapons.

"I made it clear that wasn't going to happen and they left me alone."

Cosma re-opened Uptown Auto Specialists on Monday. There was a lot of debris to be cleaned up but no structural damage.

With the hundreds of broken down and waterlogged vehicles scattered around New Orleans, it would appear that auto repair shops are primed for a banner season, but Cosma said that may not be the case.

"It could be a total bust this time," he said. "All these cars have been sitting around in this (stuff) for so long. Typically when we have a storm cars are maybe two days in the water and you get them drug in and we take them apart immediately. But these cars have been sitting in the water or been wet for a month. A lot more cars are going to be totaled than in previous times."

Cosma, however, said his most pressing concern is providing financially for the 10 people he employs.

"As an employer you're responsible for all of your employees so how would you feel as an employer if you couldn't provide to your employees what you promised when you hired them? I feel like (crap). I'm responsible for 10 people and there's only so much I can do."

* * * * * * * * * *

The great hope right now, the dream that marches on our senses, that boils the bitter fuel of our hearts, is that the populace will rise up and take matters into its own hands--against the cops, against the politicians, against the feds and every last D.C. hatchet man who has hung the charred corpse of New Orleans from the rafters for no other purpose than to delight his club-footed electorate, the country club select whose charity ends at the end of their shriveling pride.

The $10,000-a-plate coven who hiss through icicle teeth to their man on the hill, "Remember the ideology. Remember what we stand for. Now is not the time to be turned into some compassionate corner slut just because a few darkies are floating in the black waters. Now is the time to stand firm and denounce that city, that place, that New Orleans. Make a call to Falwell and Robertson. Tell those 21st century Chillingworths that it's time to brand the heathens."

We feel besieged from all sides, and sometimes from within, from those we felt we could trust.

That's how Jim Monaghan, owner of Molly's at the Market, feels.

After the cops beat down that old black teacher on Bourbon Street, Nagin pulled back the newly instituted curfew of 2 a.m. to midnight.

It's for our own safety, the mayor said.

But from who?

The cops?

Or was he saying that we couldn't be trusted to behave ourselves past midnight? That the old ways of New Orleans have no place in this post-apocalyptic version of our precious home?

And if that's the case, then let's get with it and proclaim a state of anarchy. Because if the cops can't be trusted and the people can't be trusted than who, dear mayor, can be trusted?

You?

Either way, Monaghan wasn't having it. Most bars in the Quarter make the majority of their money after midnight. They were already struggling financially under the 2 a.m. curfew. So what do you think will happen to them if they're forced to blow out the candles at 12 a.m.?

Monaghan decided to challenge the new edict. He announced that he would resume his pre-Katrina hours of operations—lights out no earlier than 6 a.m.

Word quickly spread.

That was the spark.

The line in the sand.

I made a frantic call to my editor. Shit was going down. Bar owners from the Quarter, Marigny and Bywater were going to gather en masse at Molly's at midnight. They were going to drink heavy and laugh and celebrate. This is the old rite of New Orleans, the purest form of protest.

There are no firebombs or relic chants unearthed from the sixties. When we want to make a point, we twist mean smiles on our faces by way of mama booze and get with the good times. And there ain't no better way to inflame the prostates of the furious power soldiers as they approach with oil-slicked batons then to get all googly-eyed, get with the side-steppin' dance steps, glasses raised high with women hot-and-bothered to the boom-boom bass of the brass band.

This ain't a protest officer, this is New Orleans.

Word of Monaghan's plan hit the radio, TV and papers by early afternoon. And by sunset, Nagin, fearing national footage of the NOPD cops arresting these happy-go-lucky business owners, maybe croaking a few with a flurry of precision knuckle-blasts to the skull, reinstituted the 2 a.m. curfew.

No problem boys. Just a big misunderstanding. I like boobies too.

The people declared victory. But Monaghan didn't see it that way.

"It's not a victory," Monaghan said. "We still have an arbitrarily decided curfew that is killing us. Why ask us business owners to return to the Quarter if you're going to put a curfew in place? People ask me if I've gone to talk to Nagin. Why the fuck should I go to Nagin? We voted him in to serve us. He should come to us. I'm sick of people treating politicians as if somehow they're better than us. This is not a papacy. I just hope more leaders materialize out of the citizenry. We're a city without a government right now. It's time to take things into our own hands."

There's one more important point to make--for all of those news reports now claiming that things weren't actually as bad as first reported, that the Superdome wasn't actually as hellish as the news made it out to be—they're fucking lies perpetrated by public officials looking to cover their tracks.

A sergeant with the National Guard, who lives in the back of my building, spent 11 days in the Superdome and said it was every bit as terrifying as reported. Yes, there were guns and shootings and rapes, maybe not baby-rapes, but rapes nonetheless.

I've read reports that police can't confirm these supposed rapes. Well how the fuck are you going to track down the rape victims now that they're spread out across the country? Their homes have been destroyed, family members lost and for some reason these cops think they are going to call up and make a report?

It is now in the best interests of the Bush administration and Republican whores like Rush Limbaugh and Sean Hannity to say, "These were just wild accusations by a Democratic city, a BLACK city, to make Bush look bad."

As a reporter on the ground in New Orleans, I am telling you to tell anybody who will listen that from what I've heard from the people who lived through the aftermath of Katrina, that it was just as bad, if not worse, than reported.

Ignore the talking points.

As for our own politicians--anyone in office during Katrina is in the electorate's crosshairs. Every single politician is targeted.

I like Nagin and applauded his raucous radio interview, his human outpouring for help. I spoke with people trapped in the city and they said his curse-laden tirade gave them hope. But before the storm, he blew it. Last year, Hurricane Ivan narrowly missed the chance to destroy us. Yet, even with that close call, Nagin failed to institute an evacuation plan though many were handed to him on a silver platter.

* * * * * * * * *

NO officials ripped for failing to activate Amtrak evacuation plan
By Richard A. Webster New Orleans CityBusiness Staff Writer

October 6, 2005 -- They gave New Orleans city officials an affordable plan to evacuate 30,000 low-income, elderly and homeless people, said New Orleans attorney Val Exnicios.

But city officials failed to take advantage of it and as a result thousands of needy evacuees were lost in the tempest of Hurricane Katrina.

"I can tell you unequivocally I watched Mayor (C. Ray) Nagin lie on CNN when he said there was never a plan to evacuate these people," Exnicios said. "For whatever reason no one pulled the trigger and instituted the emergency evacuation plan we came up with."

The proposed emergency evacuation plan put together by a coalition of private citizens and public officials called for trains and buses to transport about 30,000 refugees out of the city.

Amtrak agreed to provide passenger cars free while the Regional Transit Authority agreed to supply buses, said Rusty Wirth, a counselor with the New Orleans Mission.

"We gave the plan to the city and they said it's a really good idea and then they sat there and twiddled their thumbs and never took the steps to put it in motion," Wirth said. "The Friday before the hurricane we had a meeting with the Red Cross and held training sessions for evacuation with the trains but it never got that far along."

Instead, floodwaters swamped the buses and no one could get to the Amtrak station, Exnicios said.

"I'm dumbfounded."

Martha Kegel, executive director of the nonprofit Unity of Greater New Orleans, said she watched as the most vulnerable people were left behind to plead for their lives in a drowning city.

"There's no doubt many people died who shouldn't and wouldn't have died had they been evacuated," Kegel said. "The city sent buses to the New Orleans Mission to take people to the Superdome but that wasn't the evacuation plan we talked about with the city."

New Orleans city officials did not return calls for comment.

Marc Magliari, Chicago-based spokesman for Amtrak, said the company was willing to help with the evacuation.

"There will be congressional investigations to answer any questions," Magliari said.

It all began with Hurricane Ivan, said U.S. District Judge Jay Zainey, a longtime advocate for the homeless.

As Ivan barreled toward New Orleans in September 2004, shelters such as the Mission and Ozanam Inn struggled to house as many of the nearly 10,000 homeless men, women and children as possible.

The city did not help the homeless at all until the 11th hour when it opened the Superdome as a shelter, Kegel said. Had Ivan been a more powerful storm and hit New Orleans directly it would have been too little, too late.

In late May, Zainey convened the first of many meetings to address the problem. The informal gatherings were attended by Exnicios, Wirth, Kegel, Kay Wilkins, chief executive of the Red Cross Southeast Louisiana Chapter; Col. Terry Ebbert, director of homeland security for New Orleans; Dr. Kevin Stephens, director of the New Orleans Health Department; and Joseph Matthews, New Orleans chief of the Office of Emergency Preparedness.

"The city didn't have a hurricane emergency evacuation committee so we formed one ourselves to try and deal with the issue of getting homeless out of city," said Exnicios.

"We counted up the number of buses available and passenger cars from Amtrak and it all came up to between 25,000 and 30,000 people we could get out of town. It's a drop in the bucket but we figured we had 12 months to come up with a better plan to get more people out for the next hurricane season."

Exnicios said Stephens secured the agreement with Amtrak to provide passenger cars at no cost to the city.

"He was the impetus for the whole thing," Exnicios said. "When Ivan was threatening he asked FEMA what the first thing he should do was and the guy from FEMA said, 'If I were you I'd order 100,000

body bags. It's not going to be enough but it will be a good start.' Stephens' response was that was unacceptable and he was going to try to come up with a plan to get people out of the city."

Once Amtrak and RTA agreed to assist with the evacuation efforts, the committee placed the plan in the hands of Matthews, who as head of OEP was in charge of coordinating evacuations, Exnicios said.

Amtrak agreed to transport evacuees to Hammond where they would be transported to local shelters. Matthews balked and insisted he did not have the authority to compel other OEP officials to accept evacuees from outside their parishes, Exnicios said.

"I talked to Matthews 10 days before Katrina hit and said I understood what he's saying but the bottom line is we got a killer hurricane coming and we have the means of getting the people out of the city so just implement the damn plan," Exnicios said. "Let's get them out of Dodge and when they show up in Hammond or Ponchatoula or Baton Rouge, the OEP directors will have to deal with them once they're there. I don't know how they can not accept them and or transport them to whatever shelters may be available."

Shortly before Hurricane Katrina made landfall, Exnicios and Zainey met with Matthews, who assured them buses would be provided to evacuate the homeless from New Orleans.

"We sat across the table from him and Matthews said, 'Don't worry about it. It's done. I guarantee you we'll have buses and or trains available.' We both left happy," said Exnicios. "It was a tragic comedy as it turns out."

As Katrina approached, Zainey said he felt comfortable a more solid plan was in place compared with the days of Ivan.

"I know Chief Matthews supposedly followed up with Amtrak and they had very positive meetings," Zainey said. "I felt pretty confident Amtrak would happen and very confident

buses would happen."

In the end, buses arrived at the New Orleans Mission, not to evacuate the homeless but to transport them to the Superdome. No one involved with crafting the evacuation plan knows what happened.

"At least the homeless weren't stranded on the streets as they were a year ago during Ivan when a plan was nonexistent," Zainey said. "Unfortunately they were trapped in the Superdome like everyone else and unable to evacuate."

"We needed another year to work out the kinks in the plan," said Vicki Judice, director of public policy for Unity of Greater New Orleans. "We were so close. It was just so disappointing because at the least they could have used Amtrak. When the storm hit and nothing happened we were all just incredulous."

* * * * * * * * * *

We have a mayoral election in February. Unfortunately, no one knows how it will take place as 80 percent of our population is dispersed across the country, the majority of whom will never return.

This is a city that has been forced to rebuild itself from square one.

But what the hell?

For those of us who have committed themselves to seeing it through, we have the chance to rebuild a better city. And whatever form it takes, it will remain the weirdest, most ungodly city in the land-trapped 48. No matter the challenges and lack of federal assistance, we hold dear our reputation as the last true outpost of depravity and un-American activity in this uber-patriotic, Bush-inspired sinkhole.

A few weeks before Katrina, I took a four-day vacation in Chicago. At the time I was miserable in New Orleans, stuck in a rut and once again contemplating evacuation. You see, everyone in New Orleans has a love/hate relationship with this city. It affords you freedom and excess but beats you down without mercy. Only the strong survive. Get your kicks but take your beating without tears.

Well, I was at the end of my rope and by the end of the year I planned a move back to Chicago. But like all the previous times I considered leaving, New Orleans stepped up and sucked me back in.

How could I leave her in her most dire of moments? The idea is a sin in itself.

For those who have the financial ability to return and choose not to--Fuck you.

For those who question why money should be spent to rebuild a city trapped between a lake and the Gulf of Mexico--Fuck you.

By that logic all of southern Florida should be forsaken as should San Francisco and Los Angeles once the big Quake comes. And the coast of North Carolina as well. And cities

that choose to tease terrorists with tall buildings and thriving centers of commerce.
The fantastic pioneer spirit of the U.S. will die once we tell communities built in fragile
plains that we are helpless, that our technological expertise is worthless.

Are they saying we can't build better levees or that they simply don't want to? That
they'd rather save it in favor of Alaskan bridges to nowhere and slut-romping Vegas ex-
cursions for limp-dick grandpa politicians?

Why help the Tsunami victims?

The assholes had it coming.

Why assist the goddamn Africans?

Shit man, they live in a country populated by HIV-drooling monkeys.

If New Orleans is the doomed city so many now claim it is, if that is now the prevailing common knowledge, that this was a boondoggle from the start, why didn't the feds
evacuate us decades ago? Or better yet, why didn't they listen to our pleas for help? Why
did Bush, every fucking year he has been in office, cut our levee protection funding?
Why have we been allowed to exist?

You know why? Because this is the most unique of all American cities. Because the safe
couple in wherever-you-want-to-imagine-safe-couples-live, they need a place like New
Orleans. It gives them a refuge to escape to, a place of freedom where they can play in
the dreams of their youth. It makes them smile, to know that there are people out there
forever embracing that foolish feeling that once cradled them in its wild warmth.

So many years ago.

And despite our corrupt reputation, despite the brochures handed out to newly minted
politicians touting all the possibilities—the graft, the kickbacks, the bribes and legs-be-
hind-the-back limousine sex acts—we are no worse than what goes down in D.C., where
the honorable representatives and senatorial sages wave those stars and stripes high to
divert attention from their newfound love of Big Easy femurs, when once a double-ended
dildo did just fine.

But no matter.

Call us corrupt.

And we will call you unoriginal.

You decide which is worse.

You see, we have a true culture.

We are not a faceless assembly of sky-rises and Gucci penis pumps.

I am a New Orleanian for life and anyone who denigrates my commitment to this modern day Atlantis, in the immortal words of my dear friend Sneaky Pete--Stay out of New
Orleans.

You think we were deranged beforehand, well brother, you should get a load of us now.

Pre-Katrina, we never really considered ourselves a part of the U.S. And now, all pretense is gone.

We are a sovereign nation.

To the rest of the country--have at it, we're done with the bullshit.

Our hearts are as big as ever and if the time comes when you find yourself in need, we will extend our arms and donate the last of our dirty dollars. You cradled our bloodied heads in our greatest time of desperation and for that we are forever grateful. But it is our wish to disassociate ourselves from the cretins and power-mongers and biblical wretches pounding the unearthed skulls of our recently ravaged and historical corpses.

Leave us the fuck alone.

Get it?

If we are meant to live the remainder of our days in the sludge of post-destruction, we will do so to the romp of a second-line, the smell of a crawfish boil and with the taste of iced-beer rocking our lips.

Defend New Orleans--our call to arms.

Whatever New Orleans is in its present form, and whatever form it will take in the future, it is ours.

Do not underestimate our lack of sanity.

Second Entry

November 4, 2005
The Evolution of the Second Thumb

I'M GONNA PICK ME OUT A NICE TALL
TREE TO CLIMB
WHERE I'LL WAIT
...
....
...

WITH GUN IN ONE HAND
AND A BOTTLE OF HORNITOS IN THE OTHER.

THAT'S MY LEVEE SYSTEM.

FUCK OFF.

Well, the hoariest of all whores has wrapped her spider-veined legs around my head. The squeeze is on.

Our dear Gov. Kathleen Babineaux Blanco blocked landlord evictions through Oct. 25. Give the people a chance was the idea. So the landlords sat back and waited in claw-footed bathtubs filled with cow blood. When the time came, they would rise from these shallow pools of corpuscles like Martin Sheen in Apocalypse Now.

We tenants beseeched the Guvnuh to extend the blockade but she made with the baby-talk and said, "Oogy boogy boo. Go fuck yourselves."

And the banshee screams of landlords on the hunt swept the city. Thousands of eviction notices moved through the courts.

Sure, some landlords had just cause. Many tenants had abandoned their apartments or houses leaving behind piles of clothing and other materials collecting mold that rotted the structures from the inside. These landlords had no choice.

And then there are people like my landlord, Lisa Mellion. My building escaped the storm without a scratch or a soaked piece of dry wall. No water, no looting, no blown out windows. Nada.

So why would she evict all of her tenants?

Easy answer.

Money.

As we live in the only untouched and dry slip of land in New Orleans, rental property is at a premium. Tens of thousands of people want back into New Orleans but there is no place to live. More importantly, those with the means to return are willing to pay big bucks. So landlords such as my own evict their current tenants, triple the rent and grab some fast cash to fulfill fast dreams, have Dr. Fixum slap on that third tit they've dreamt of since they were little girls, hiding under their parents' bed, listening as Mommy and the egg beater made little can openers.

It helps that Louisiana is one of only a handful of backwards states that allow no-cause evictions. No reason necessary. Give proper notice and you're out on the street.

Hello? Ms. Landlord? Why's all my shit out on the sidewalk crawling with maggots?

Oh. I see. You left a note.

Let's see what you have to say....

"Suck it Pony Boy."

32

Hmmm. That doesn't make any sense at all. But there appears to be an addendum to this here simple note. This should clear up all of my confusion. Let's read it together.

"P.S. God hates you."

Ouch.

For people who have no lease such as myself, five to ten days notice is required. I got three.

Yeah, we're going to court.

But first I tried appealing to my landlord's humanity.

"I understand you want us out to renovate the building but I need more than three days."

"How many days do you need? Five?" she asked.

"Five? Are you crazy? I need at least two weeks. In case you haven't noticed, you living in California and all, but New Orleans has been destroyed by a hurricane. You can't find a U-Haul or storage space much less a goddamn apartment for a reasonable price."

"I'll see what I can do and call you back," she said.

Two minutes later.

"Rich? It's Lisa. My lawyer has instructed me to proceed with the eviction process."

"You can't just give us three days notice and expect that to be enough."

"I didn't do anything illegal," she said, calm as a milk crate.

"How about immoral?" I lashed out. "You don't find anything wrong about kicking us to the streets when our lives have been torn apart and we're just trying to survive? You think that's the right thing to do?"

"It's a business decision," said the milk crate to the aspiring serial killer.

"Did you know that I'm a journalist?"

On Monday, my newspaper will hit the stands and on the cover is a story about how my lovely landlord raped one of my fellow tenants.

* * * * * * * * * *

First wave of evictions hits New Orleans
By Richard A. Webster New Orleans CityBusiness Staff Writer

November 7, 2005 -- On Oct. 29, Jonathan Most received a notice to vacate his apartment. He was given until Nov. 1 to leave the premises.

"I'm being forced to find a new place and figure out a way to move all of my stuff out with no notice," the 32-year-old Most said.

Most's Uptown apartment building escaped the wrath of Hurricane Katrina, he said.

"There was no damage whatsoever — no mold, no holes in the roof, no blown-out windows, no sewage or water backup. It wasn't even looted. It looked like I had never left."

When Most moved back into his apartment Oct. 16, he called his landlord to ask about rent.

"The only reply I got was an eviction notice," Most said.

His landlord, Lisa Mellion with Magnolia Properties New Orleans LLC, based in San Leandro, Calif., said she would not talk about the case based on the advice of her attorney. In her eviction letter she expressed a desire to reclaim the property in order to proceed with renovations begun prior to Hurricane Katrina.

"I don't do anything illegally," she said. "It was a business decision."

On Nov. 3, the First City Court for Orleans Parish in Algiers heard the first of what is expected to be thousands of eviction claims from the East Bank.

On the eve of the first day of hearings, presiding Judge Charles Imbornone prepared for the tidal wave.

"I'm losing my mind on my own house and adjusters right now," Imbornone said. "All I'm doing is saying prayers and hoping I do the right thing."

A bill strengthening landlord rights to evict tenants who have abandoned their living space is making its way through the Legislature.

For people like Most and Mellion the "right thing" depends on what side they are on.

Laura Tuggle, an attorney with Southeast Louisiana Legal Services, said Louisiana law heavily favors the landlord.

Louisiana is one of only a handful of states that allows "no-cause" evictions. Landlords can evict month-to-month tenants with no lease for any reason on five to 10 days notice.

"Even in a normal world it's very difficult to do anything in that time frame," Tuggle said. "But in a post-Katrina world it's downright impossible, especially for a low-income person. There's no housing available and people can't even find a U-Haul truck or a storage facility."

Even if a lease is in place, landlords do not need a specific reason for eviction, Tuggle said.

"I'm hoping judges may show some greater leniency in terms of giving people more time to move out," she said.

Imbornone said even though Hurricane Katrina created unique situations he is bound by the law and can't provide undue leniency.

Tuggle estimated landlords come out on top more than 90 percent of the time in eviction cases.

Tammy Esponge, director of the Apartment Association of Greater New Orleans, agreed judges rarely rule in favor of the tenant in Orleans Parish.

But, she said, landlords are getting a bad rap. The biggest misconception is that they are throwing people out of their homes for no reason or out of naked greed.

"Landlords are concerned about properties that have been damaged by water and mold

34

but they can't get inside to clean them because their tenants have abandoned them and are out of contact," Esponge said. "They're not looking to evict anyone from undamaged properties unless they didn't pay the rent or violated the lease. There may be a few smaller owners doing it but I can say most of our members are absolutely not."

According to Most's lease, 30 days notice is required for either the landlord or tenant to break it.

Most said he received three days notice even though he paid September's rent before evacuating.

He said he tried to pay October's rent but was rebuffed by Darrell M. Mellion in an Oct. 6 e-mail.

"We are awaiting an inspection by our insurance company to ascertain any structural damage to the building (and) are asking that you not return until the building has been inspected," Darrell Mellion wrote. "We are trying our best to expedite the inspection, however, due to the magnitude and number of individuals affected by the catastrophe we are not sure when this will happen. Due to conditions we are not accepting rent at this time. Thank you in advance for understanding."

Most said he suspects Lisa Mellion is kicking him out in order to raise the rent. Esponge refutes the charge.

"Landlords are not looking to raise rents," she said. "Absolutely not. Maybe some smaller owners have raised rents but not the 40 (percent) to 50 percent increases they're quoting on TV. Rents may raise 5 to 10 percent but that's over time."

Tuggle said she has seen many current cases in which tenants in undamaged properties have been evicted so landlords can jack up the rents and little can be done about it.

The Louisiana price gouging statute applies only to goods and services but not residential property.

Louisiana law also allows landlords to recoup rent from tenants in undamaged properties even for the month of September when the city was under a mandatory evacuation, Tuggle said.

"Now would be a good time for the state to look at and reform our landlord and tenant laws," Tuggle said. "If not now than when? One avenue is to limit price gouging but if you don't close the back door and place limits on 'no-cause' evictions, landlords will be free to evict for any reason and raise rents. In legal proceedings you have the concept of reasonableness but what was reasonable before is just not reasonable now."

As for Most, he has little choice but to pack his belongings and search for a new home unless a judge rules in his favor.

Most said he still has never entertained the notion of leaving New Orleans.

"I want to stay here and help rebuild," he said. "I have friends who have lost a lot more than me and I have friends I haven't gotten in touch with yet and I don't know if they're

OK. Rule No. 1 I've learned in New Orleans is that if you're cool with the city, the city's cool with you. I don't wish ill on anybody but what Lisa's doing is extremely wrong and something needs to be done about it."

* * * * * * * * *

Hell. That's just how it goes in the new New Orleans, a foul place if there ever was one. Survival of the fittest and the godless children of Greenspan and Milton Friedman. That's why the gun shop owners walk around dripping in gold while crude oil seeps out of their pockets.

Hand sanitizer is now passé. Guns are the latest and most fashionable accessories and, with God's grace, I will join the fashionable set as soon as I get my '88 Ford Bronco II running for more than five days straight without the wretched pile of mechanical debris breaking down.

Maybe I'll get the gun first and put the truck out of its misery. And a few insurance adjustors while I'm at it.

Carve myself out a new orifice. Give the man and his henchmen a different option by which to fuck me.

Variety is the key to any unhealthy relationship.

Stress is the new drug, injected straight into the heart with a titanium-edged turkey baster. And oh boy it do pack a whollop and shakes the rafters of the bones. My skin is falling off but I'm told it's nothing more than a permanent side effect, so no worries.

But too much stress and you'd go all Unabomber which is why the lone freaks in town congregated in dark mass in front of Molly's on Decatur Street this Halloween for a little Central Park wildin'.

Halloween has always been a high holy holiday in New Orleans. But this Halloween, the first after the storm, we were after something more. We wanted to let it bleed.

None of us knew what was happening. We were a new species trying to find its way in a place that held all the old familiar sights and scents but reeked of an institutionalized perfume of confinement, rubber and mosquito sweat.

We told ourselves we were ok.

We told ourselves we were keeping it together.

But we were the least capable of diagnosing the sickness that was growing from within. It has only been two months. What the hell do we know? We don't know shit. We're lost and desperately holding onto each other. If we keep tight and group together in numbers, maybe the light won't shine in, maybe we won't find ourselves alone, in a room, cordoned off from our necessary distractions, vulnerable to this reality, this grim new life, flipping through Guns and Ammo magazine in search of a solution.

Stay blind.

Stay stupid.

Stay ignorant.

For now.

For just a few more weeks.

Because I got a feeling,

When we open our eyes,

We're all gonna fall apart.

And fall away

From each other.

Halloween was the first sanctioned holiday following the storm. It was the first chance for all of us to get together in one mad pack, out there in the dark, in masks and costumes.

Let it bleed.

And we did.

Molly's.

Ground Zero.

There's always been something special about Halloween in New Orleans. It perfectly suits our natural tendencies towards strong drink and a dip in the other world.

But this Halloween, we were already in that other world, unsure of the new laws and morals and what was expected of us by the new gods who we have yet to identify.

So best let it all hang fucking loose.

Just to be sure.

And it went off.

Any poor driver who turned onto Decatur Street heard dozens of feet dancing on his roof, saw fat corpses humping each other on his hood, tongues washing his windshield with labia-like precision. And behind him there were 20 more car-drivin' fools, a metallic slaughterhouse for the disconnected survivors of Katrina who didn't know whether they were supposed to be cannibals or the disciples of Caligula.

Fire-breathers and flame-jugglers stumbled in front of the lead car splashing swarms of sparks off the chrome shell.

The driver gripped the wheel, gritted his teeth and set his eyes forward, to some far-off spot in the distance.

Keep it cool man.

Keep it cool and steady.

You've seen this shit on Discovery Channel.

You know what they're after.

They're after your heart.

They're after your pride.

So keep it cool, man.

Real cool.

Blood trickled out the side of the driver's mouth as he dug his teeth deep into the thick meat of his tongue.

The passenger, a younger kid, stared at a pair of blood-streaked breasts mashed up against the glass, just a foot from his sex-crazed brain.

All that blood.

All that flesh.

Oh God man.

Keep it cool.

Real cool.

Two women in voodoo garb slithered up the hood of an Army Humvee and onto the desert brown roof where they did reptilian things to each other, making salamander movements and gecko gesticulations.

Up until this point, the weekend warriors, the National Guardsmen, they thought we were sort of normal.

Sure, we like to drink, but so do they.

A good-time port for good-time soldiers.

"Hey Mom, these people down here ain't so strange. Don't believe what you read. New Orleans is a cool town. You and Pop should come down and visit."

But that night, that Halloween, these salty children of the click-click, square-jawed bombardiers saw the truth.

"Mom?"

"Hey baby. How's your Halloween?"

"Mom….I need a crucifix…my gun….it's no use…"

"Kenny? What's wrong? Why are you crying like a 12-year-old girl?"

"These people…Mommy…..they're not right. I can't……."

"Kenny, pull yourself together."

"I've seen things Mom. I've seen things tonight. These things I've seen….."

"Kenny, now you pull yourself together. Remember what Toby Keith said, 'I got grenades for testicles and I piss red, white and blue. Ain't nuthin' but a raghead that I'm urinatin' on for you.' Remember that baby…..baby…..Kenny…..what was that click?"

"Tell Toby Keith I love him momma…."

BOOM!!!

We showed our shit on Halloween and it was a glorious coming out party.

After the street madness we hit One Eyed Jacks and lost our minds to the sounds of the Morning Forty Federation.

But these moments are fleeting and afterwards it was back to business. Back to politics, strategy and revenge.

Every Wednesday Jim Monaghan and Harry Anderson of Night Court fame host a town forum at Anderson's speakeasy on the corner of Decatur and Esplanade. French Quarter residents come out in force to rage and vent at their no-good, eunuch leaders. Anderson, now a fat, bloated, bitter alcoholic, works the crowd like Phil Donahue while his fortyish, sexy-from-a-distance wife sucks down cocktails and smokes.

They try to keep it civil and organized but we're all too raw and too drunk.

At the last meeting Monaghan lost it, targeting the heart of it, all of our frustration and all of our inebriation.

He stumbled through the crowd with the microphone, imploring people to speak their minds, to voice some truth to power.

"I think what we need to do is start a letter writing campaign," one woman said. "I think we need to…."

"No!" Monaghan said. "No! These people don't care about fucking letters. And who in the hell is going to deliver our letters? We need to make them understand the shit we're going through, that we are the people, that we are the ones in power…"

Some acid-happy kid a few feet from me in the back of the room shouted, "You're all idiots! Nothing's going to change. We need to dance and put ribbons on horses! You fools are trying to tell the suicide cases to be happy? You're wasting your damn time! People deserve to suffer! They deserve to befriend weasels and make love to weasels and have weasel babies that refuse to behave or eat their vegetables! I have a weasel penis and a camel hump filled with MDMA! Suck on my teets!"

The crowd tried to shout him down. His friends tried to pull him down. Jim Monaghan didn't try anything. He just told that kid to get the fuck out.

In a different time, I would have reveled in the little punk's incoherent disruption. But during this post-storm era, there wasn't anything rebellious in the foam spilling out of his mouth. Not now. The little fuck was nothing more than a stilt-walker pretending to be a titan.

I hated him.

It didn't matter that I agreed with him, that this collection of people in the Night Court speakeasy were involved in a pointless exercise, a toothless, civic daisy chain.

In normal times, in the old days, the days before all of this happened, the kid's insane LSD rantings would have put a smile on my face. But when Jim Monaghan came charging towards him, his eyes fiery with purpose and conviction and whiskey, suddenly the get-cool games of old meant nothing to me.

This is not what we need.

You dumb little fuck.

Go climb a roof and make with your stuttering poetry and pretentious mop-hair nihilism.

These people in this room, they are fighting for something.

But after attending three meetings, I too came to the quick conclusion that nothing was ever going to come from these hamburger-helping congregations.

But out of respect I attended one more meeting, bringing with me a friend. I promised him something wild.

"You should have seen the last one," I said. "This crazed little fuck went nuts and got kicked out."

But nothing happened. Monaghan was sober and nobody jumped up in a psychedelic seizure filled with goofy hate.

"This is boring," I said. "Let's get the fuck out of here."

On the other side of the Quarter, in a stately courtyard with a garden and waterfall, an older, sweater-around-the-neck crowd presented themselves to Councilmember Jackie Clarkson, the Tammy Faye Baker of the political set. Part Elvira, part Bride of Franken-stein, this weeble-wobble woman shuffled through the crowd making like the benevolent dictator, all glad-handing and back-patting with a predator's grin.

In her monstrous tenure on the City Council she rid the Quarter of the tap-dancin' kids and tried to eradicate the tarot card readers and homeless.

She longed for the days of old, the stately days, the genteel ways when the bright-eyed lords lorded over the rheumy yellow cataracts of the poor.

Divert your eyes!

Divert your eyes!

The manor is on the move!

I received an invitation to attend this meeting of the minds at this swank mini-mansion in the Quarter, a few blocks off of Bourbon Street.

It was time for the rich to hold their own post-Katrina strategy session over wine and cheese and the rubber-band taught facial skin of "those whose age shall not be men-tioned."

They chuckled and perched brandy snifters in birdbath wrists. They betrayed no urgency for change. They betrayed no desperation.

No one got weird on spiked punch.

No one lost their shit.

No one did anything in this bankrupt congregation of the assured and placidly comfort-able.

I hit the bartender up for a double gin and tonic and moved like a shadow through the courtyard and up the stone stairs to the kitchen. The bluebloods paid me no notice. I was a gin-scented breeze.

After haunting the first floor of the host's urban palace, I drifted back onto the surface of the courtyard, searching for some trace of Katrina, evidence that we were all inhabiting the same apocalyptic city.

"So why are you here?" I asked a girl sitting in a metal chair next to the fountain. She was young but didn't seem out of place in this marbleized collection of high society. She was fresh, her skin unblemished, but from her sensible heels to her potted plant haircut, she looked like a place-holder, a twenty-something dilettante yearning for the day when she too could be a plastic, fifty-something harpy, rich with power and the ability to indulge herself in the self-righteous smarm of old world wisdom.

She had no business being young.

"My boyfriend brought me," she said.

And here comes her boyfriend, tightly permed and pressed and slicked back and Gucci-model ready.

"My name is Charlie," he said, extending a hand.

"What's up? I'm Rich. So do you feel as queasy as I do hanging out with these cow-eyed money-whores?"

Silence.

"What do you mean?" he asked.

I laughed. He didn't.

I'm that acid-happy asshole.

"Nothing," I said.

And I moved on.

And then came the big moment. It was time for Queen Jackie Clarkson to hold court and address her minions. She stood atop the stone stairs in her big-buttoned skirt-suit and creamed a photo-op smile on her billboard face.

"Thank you!" she bellowed. "Thank you!"

And the throngs applauded, rattling their skeletal hands together, orbital eyes bulging out of their sockets with a single-minded fervor.

(Editor's note: The following quotes attributed to Sweet Jackie are products of the booze-drenched brain of the author. They are complete fabrications of a disturbed soul and bear no resemblance to reality. She is an honorable public servant beyond reproach. The author should be flogged like a goat in Jackson Square. We now return, dear reader, to Jumpin' Jackie Flash's Sermon on the Mount.)

"Please take your seats my precious people. Oh, my wonderful people. So glitzy. So bluish of blood. I want to polish your marble heads and put you all on pedestals in showroom windows so the world can truly see how New Orleans do shine! But that's not why I'm here today. I'm here to give you my promise to faithfully represent your needs and desires, to strive to keep the Quarter pure for all condo owners. For now and for eternity!" Jackie shouted. "I promise to promulgate the lifestyle of the rich and sheltered. This is a new age for New Orleans, a new opportunity to restore the Quarter to the grand old pooh-bah days when we could safely meander down Royal and Chartres without fear of being touched or brushed upon by the soiled and sullen."

The crowd erupted in a flurry of golf claps and clattering dentures.

"I promise to rid Rampart Street of the noisy boom boom clubs and replace them with origami shops and potpourri vendors. No longer shall we, the diamond-studded gods and goddesses of old New Orleans be forced to associate with the rabble. Someone once said, 'Let them eat cake.' But I believe if you let them eat cake they'll only get comfortable and want something more, like pies or pralines. So I say, 'Let them eat what we tell them to eat.' Give them crackers one day and toenails the next. For we are the keepers of the old ways, the noble ways, the pearly white necklace ways! The true heroes of New Orleans!"

I had placed my tape recorder on the edge of the stage to catch every syllable of Clarkson's wrong sentiments. But 20 minutes into her harangue I decided enough was enough. No more goddammit.

I shoved my way through the butterscotch-sucking masses, grabbed my recorder and headed towards the exit. But first, one last stop at the bar.

"Gin and tonic, double," I told the bartender, a septuagenarian black man in a bowtie. He mixed it up in a plastic cup, tossed in a lime and placed it on the table. I picked it up and threw down two dollars.

"What a bunch of assholes," I said, motioning back to the crowd.

Instead of the chummy, insider camaraderie I expected between two down-on-their-luck working guys, the bartender turned his back to me and pretended to take stock of the remaining wine bottles. And he didn't turn around until I was at a safe distance, inches from the exit.

I stumbled out onto the street, drunk and disgusted, and slammed the gate shut behind me.

The crash spooked the blue-blood crowd.

Someone shouted, "The heathens are attacking! Protect the queen!"

I slung back half of my drink and threw the rest on the sidewalk.

On the other side of the gate, the two older women whose job it was to check invitations murmured to each other.

"Did he have an invite?"

"I don't know. But if he did I shudder for the future of New Orleans."

"Don't worry. Jackie has plans for his kind."

"I hope so because he made me uneasy. He didn't belong here."

"Don't worry Margaret. That kind, they don't last. They die young. They all have sex with each other, sometimes all at once. They do those drugs and drink each other's sweat. They have no future."

"I hope you're right Julia. Because the only hope for New Orleans lies with people like us, like Jackie. All we can hope for is that this evil, younger generation dies off like they're supposed to. And from the looks of that guy, they don't have long to go."

I stood in the middle of the street, under the street lamp's glare and found myself agreeing.

Maybe those two old bags are right.

And maybe, just maybe, there's more to you Jackie, than meets the eye.

Maybe it was the nine gin and tonics I had consumed, maybe it was the joker's wild ecstasy pill I popped, or maybe it was the way your black and white crown of thorns exploded out of your head, forming a halo of spider webs and poisoned cotton candy.

Whatever the reason, dear Jackie oh Jackie, I believe I have fallen in love with you.

No, I don't believe, I know.

At first I tried to fight these dirty feelings. I told myself there could be no future between a drunken wretch like me and a hateful siren such as you.

We come from different worlds. I am a denizen of the low places, a self-pleasuring hedonist with an intimate knowledge of the unclean masses you hold in pure contempt.

I have struggled with the logistics of crossing the chasm that separates our world-views. You hate the poor. You instructed the police to lay heavy on the homeless, going so far as to take away the benches in front of St. Louis Cathedral in Jackson Square, agreeing to return them only after you welded a third arm in the middle to prevent them from lying down. You railed against a plan to transform Rampart Street, long an avenue lined with boarded and abandoned buildings, overrun with dealers and whores, into an entertainment district jumping with jazz clubs celebrating the musical heritage of New Orleans.

And why did you do these things….

Because you are a realtor overpowered by a craven lust for high property values and conformity.

You have publicly expressed your precious desire to return to the good old days, the 1950s when the French Quarter was a genteel place, a snow-white land of lords and ladies, when the only hucksters plying their trade in Jackson Square were non-threatening artists who massaged their canvases with horse-hair brushes, tenderizing the final touches on pretty pictures of trees and flowers.

It was a grand time when the blackies shined shoes and averted their eyes from your kind. It was a grand time when the rights of man applied only to those who carried gold in their cheeks.

And I know how hard it must be for you, now that the grand times are dead, now that you and your kind are forced to meet in fortified courtyards, sipping on spirits and assuring each other that it is not too late, that there remains hope.

But those people who wrapped themselves around your every word, they are old and dying, a constituency of the frail, relics of the old ways.

And that comforted me. I want your kind to follow the light of the moon as it breaks on the Mississippi River.

Follow the light.

The lazy, old-money slags who shield themselves from OUR New Orleans in million-dollar condos and stately mansions--tell them they can walk on water and tomorrow we'll go bobbing for their plastic faces in another post-disaster dawn.

But I was a fool to think your disciples are limited to obscenely wealthy geriatrics, for I have met their offspring and they are legion.

Oh Jackie dear Jackie, how I hated you. But I now realize that in this post-storm apocalypse, you are the light that will lead the righteous and predestined to the promise land.

So I figure it's time to get on board. It's time to unite our disparate worlds for the greater good.

I want to ravage you dear Jackie!

I want to cradle your butterball body in my quivering arms and rip off the clown buttons of your blazer with my teeth, exposing your nude-colored brassiere and the freckles on your chest that form the constellation of a "For Sale" sign.

We will lie down in a bed of promissory notes where I will tickle your nipples with condominium contracts.

"This feels wrong Richard," you'll say in that cracked-vocal cord tone of yours that has ruptured the eardrums of thousands of struggling souls.

"Shhhh," I'll whisper, wiping away the blood trickling out of my nose. "Let's communicate with our bodies. I want to hear your bosom sing and the chorus of your inner thighs. You trollish temptress!"

And if I don't call you the next day it's only because I am lying in a ball on the floor in some dark place, mumbling, reliving every sweaty moment we shared.

And if I don't call you the day after, not to worry--it's only because I am afraid of my feelings.

And if I don't call you in a week it will be because I found a marble in the street and am spending most of my time trying to track down its rightful owner.

But don't worry. I'll eventually call because you mean the world to me and that moment we shared was something special and will serve as an example to our ravaged city that even the worst of enemies can put aside their differences and come together in a sleazy flesh-pretzel for the greater good.

And don't worry. I won't tell anybody that you smell like a hard-boiled egg. That's a private thing, between lovers.

Sweet Jackie.

Dear Jackie.

My high-class chickenhead.

Oh Jackie.

I alternate my boozy indulgences--one night on, one night off, sometimes two nights on, one night off. If I'm feeling really bothered, it's three nights on. And if those three nights run into a Friday then it's five days on.

Fuck it. I'm drunk seven days a week.

Drink is our friend.

It soothes the nerves.

"My car broke down today five days after I got the fucker out of the shop."

Hello Mr. Budweiser.

"I got a three-day eviction notice."

I love you Ms. Tequila.

"No one loves me."

Hey Mr. Budweiser and Ms. Tequila, what say we give that slutty friend of yours cocaine a call and get lost for a while.

Oh that numb, it comes so rarely.

Hard to say when we'll all lose it. My guess is never. My guess is that our organs will harden over time granting us immortality.

The stone people of New Atlantis.

"Please keep them at bay Mr. President! They're after our daughters and our drink!"

They are insatiable.

Inscrutable.

Indestructible.

They must be destroyed.

Did you know there remains a giant gaping hole in the 17th Street Levee?

Did you know we have yet to receive any assurance that our levee system will be rebuilt to withstand something greater than a Category 3 hurricane?

I bought myself a spotted owl the other day and rammed a fork in its head. I called him Foreshadow before his mysterious demise.

I studied his death throes and mimic the movements every night before going to bed. The new yoga.

Ahhh, these moments they do come, these wall-closing moments when our heads shrink and out comes the brain matter.

Worst of all, I have no refrigerator—it went bad after many weeks of neglect turned its contents into pestilence--and am forced to drink warm beer.

My fingers are encrusted with stomach bile.

But we grow stronger with each cut of a corner and evaporating comfort of the civilized world. There has always been pride in saying you hailed from New Orleans but now it has mutated into something more akin to a defiant statement.

A threat.

We have all adopted an unofficial symbol, the profile of a skull with a Mohawk made of steel spikes. Below the skull is a rifle and the words "Defend New Orleans." There is no sentiment that greater illustrates our collective state of mind and that is why we don't take so kindly to people like my landlord pushing her cancerous weight around.

It's why I lashed out in print (though, of course, done in the even-handed manner of a respectable journalist). It is why I tracked down and consulted the judge ruling over the cases and why the lawyer Johnny Hollywood recently hit with his car chose to represent him against our landlord as opposed to suing for vehicular assault.

We rally and we roar and we take care of each other and woe be the interloper.

We've suffered many casualties at the hands of Mother Nature but this was not a natural disaster, it was a man-made catastrophe created by the assholes who built inferior levees and the assholes who refused to give us enough money to protect our fast-eroding coast. During Katrina and Rita we lost 100 square miles of marsh, something that over time would have taken 45 years to accomplish.

But let's let the politicians get back to the business of spending billions a week to rebuild Iraq. We understand that New Orleans is too great a risk. Best to concentrate on a sure-fire winner—a country with no history of democracy, fractured by a multi-layered civil war and flanked by Iran and Syria, avowed enemies of the U.S.

That's a safe investment. A blue chip stock. A Viagra moment in time.

So as I close this latest letter from the New Atlantis, before I roll it up and slip it into my empty bottle of Jaegermeister, I'm gonna pick me out a nice tall tree to climb where I'll wait with gun in one hand and a bottle of Hornitos in the other.

That's my levee system.

Fuck off.

Addendum to previous entry:

Two matters need to be addressed.

One week ago a regular at the Balcony Bar shot himself in the head. I knew him briefly through mutual friends and random drunken conversations.

No one knows why he did it.

He had a good job and never seemed distraught.

We search for answers but they never come.

The other matter involves the Please-U restaurant on St. Charles Avenue. After Katrina looters bent heavy on the joint and ripped its insides out. It took the family that has operated it since 1976 nearly two months to get it straight. On Friday they celebrated its grand reopening.

On Sunday a fire broke out in the apartment above. The owners watched and wailed, their tortured faces bathed in the floating crimson lights of the fire engines.

Emergency responders contained the flames to the second floor but the damage had been done.

How much more can a people suffer after 80 percent of their city has been destroyed?

Mother Nature came and did her thing, but she left something behind, a presence with an insatiable lust for pain. It doesn't gain or lessen in strength like a hurricane and it doesn't follow a path. It doesn't suddenly appear, inflict damage and dissipate. It is constant. It drapes itself over those it wishes to hurt most as it eases its way into the fabric of local folklore.

As if it has always been here, among us.

I don't know how else to explain what is happening.

It's not a curse.

It is what it is.

And it is here.

Addendum to the addendum:

The suicide victim referenced in the last passage did not shoot himself in the head. He died from a bullet in the gut. He had juvenile diabetes. Blindness or the loss of a limb or limbs was his destiny. According to his friend he was a weapons expert. And it is his friend's belief, his desperate belief that this poor soul did not commit suicide, that in his extreme drunkenness he mishandled his gun and off it went.

That sounds about right to me.

It sounds comforting.

Let's leave it there.

Third Entry
November 18, 2005
Diet by Death

RAINDROPS ON TEAR DROPS.
AND SABERS IN KITTENS.
BRIGHT BLAZING GUNSHOTS AND
BULLETS ARE HITTIN'
STRANGE WOODEN PACKAGES

FILLED UP WITH SIN
THESE ARE A FEW OF MY FAVORITE THINGS

I just burned my hair lighting a cigarette on the stove, just a few hours after I got a hair-cut. Goddamn curse of New Orleans. Isn't it enough that my fleur-de-lis truck is crippled and I have no home? Now I am forced to walk about town with an unusual upward curve in my bangs.

Terrible fucking fates have pimped my pride out like a dirty bird-flu hooker hooked on glue and aluminum.

I'll go stand on my balcony for a few minutes and see how long it takes for a spear to come screaming out of the clouds and impale my throat.

One. Two. Three. Four.…...

Ow.

I now have a spear in my throat making it hard to negotiate the turns and tight corners of my soon-to-be former apartment. But woe be the assailant who tries to fuck with ol' Spear Throat. Wolverine ain't got nuthin' on me.

Or maybe he does. After all, I'll bleed to death the minute I extract this fucking spear from my jugular. Great geysers of white and red blood cells will coat the pavement around me. Children will come running to frolic in my sprinkling death, laughing and twittering in the blood-storm.

Death don't faze us no more. Death has lost its grandeur to the Ninth Ward kiddies who rode inflatable corpses through oily waters to get to the Superdome where they were promptly taken to the bathrooms for a wholesome round of hurricane rape.

But don't listen to me. I'm nothing more than a functioning drunk with a mean attitude and too much time on my hands which I use to trample the English language and conjure wretched images to illustrate mindless points about insanity, depravity and loneliness that give me an excuse to swear like a fucking shit-headed politician.

I'm a buffoon.

No one takes what I say seriously. And if they do they should quickly negotiate a three-month lease in the hurricane rape rooms.

I'm a recluse.

I'm a barfly.

I'm a downtrodden writer with a chip of Gibraltar on my sinking shoulder.

I fit right into this broken-down city.

Born into a landfill.

My office is in Jefferson Parish, in a city called Metairie, just ten minutes outside of New Orleans, off West End Boulevard, a major thoroughfare divided by a giant grassy median that once served as a park for the surrounding community. West End Boulevard leads to Lakeview, a posh neighborhood that sits off of Lake Pontchartrain. Lakeview sits in the shadow of the 17th Street Canal that gave way on the same day Katrina hit. As mentioned before--this was not a natural disaster, it was a man-made disaster. The 17th Street Canal gave way because it was built on swampland. Pilings that should have been driven deep into the earth were given shallow berth. When the waters rose it proved to be too much and everything gave way.

Stupid fucking Corps of Engineers.

Mister and Missus Lakeview returned to 10-foot-high waterlines stained on their front doors and blob-like mold spreading like syphilis. News reports focused on the Ninth Ward but the rich got hit just as bad in some parts. Take a ride through their streets. The wealthy can be seen outside of their homes in gas masks and hazmat suits, shoveling out tender memories that have dissolved into crusty piles of crap. And every shovelful is taken to the West End Boulevard neutral ground where it is dumped, creating what is now a mile-long, four-story tall pile of trees, barcaloungers, love seats, rainbow-colored kiddie toys, mattresses, shattered toilets and bathtubs, plastic outdoor pools, swing sets and several tons of long-gone house parts.

To get to my office I have to drive through a Mad Max world, an urban wasteland tortured by the laughter of ghosts and the smell of dead pirates. The red X's are omnipresent--painted on the doors and walls of the still-standing structures by the cops and National Guard to signal whether a body was found inside. The bodies.

All them bodies.
They surround us.
We can't see them,
But we know they are in our presence,
Behind the doors,
Up the stairs,
In the hidden places,
Faces fixed with that final emotion
That consumed their souls
In that last moment,
That terrible last moment.
Sometimes it's hard to shake the spirits of the storm.
Sometimes it's impossible.
But there are those who manage,

Who persevere,

Who bleed pride

When others sink into the Ambien ether.

* * * * * * * * *

Mid-City business owner is first to rise

By Richard A. Webster New Orleans CityBusiness Staff Writer

October 21, 2005 -- Darren Brooks is a hurricane pioneer, the first sign of life in the now desolate Mid-City community. If all goes according to plan, this week Brooks will reopen his bar, Brooks' Seahorse Saloon, located across the street from the front gates of the shuttered New Orleans Fairgrounds. Brooks' neighborhood is still buried by Katrina. Down Gentilly Boulevard from the Seahorse, all the local haunts — Alesia's Steak and Seafood Restaurant, Club Gentilly, Martin's Sandwich Shop and Family Sno-Ball — are boarded up. The only signs of life are a few brave gas-masked residents creating personal landfills on the sidewalk out of mattresses, lamps, recliners, bicycles, desks and brightly colored children's furniture.

Reopening a business here won't be easy, Brooks said.

"It's really quiet. I haven't seen anyone around here yet," he said. "Service for the cleanup workers is the only business right now. I guess I could move somewhere else but there is something magical about the city and hopefully this is a chance to make everything better. It would be good to be a part of that. But I don't know how a lot of these little businesses are going to make it."

Brooks and his wife, Susan, bought the Seahorse building for $270,000 and spent $200,000 on renovations. Since opening two years ago, Brooks said they made money every month except in September 2004 when Hurricane Ivan landed.

"This summer was way better than last summer," Brooks said. "Everything was on the incline."

And then Hurricane Katrina hit. Mid-City, where the Seahorse is located, took in more than 8 feet of water in spots.

Brooks said it wasn't the water or wind that did the most damage to his bar — it was the looters who unloaded three fire extinguishers, smashed more than 12 cases of beer and went to the bathroom in one of his coolers that now sits curbside along with its ruined brethren.

"The hurricane is tough but the looting just breaks your spirit," Brooks said. "It's ridiculous. You try so hard to make something nice. It makes you want to forget it all, sell out

and leave. Of course, I can't say I'm surprised. We got robbed three times in the last year and a half."

Brooks estimates the damage to his bar, including 300 pounds of rotted food, at more than $12,000. He said it will be like opening a brand new bar but he is determined to see it through.

Across the street the roof of the Fair Grounds grandstand is torn off in spots and curled back in others. Huge swaths are missing from the sides and barn structures suffered significant damage.

No timetable has been set for a return to the Fair Grounds, said Julie Koenig, director of communications for Churchill Downs. "Like a lot of New Orleans businesses there are too many unanswered questions right now," Koenig said. "Do we have a customer base, is the infrastructure there, do we have places for employees and customers to live? A lot of things we don't have answers to yet."

A few blocks from the Fair Grounds, owner James Lemarie is doing everything he can to reopen Liuzza's by the Track by early November or early December.

Hurricane Katrina flooded the Mid-City institution with about 2 feet of water and looters busted up some poker machines, an ATM and stole some liquor. But Lemarie still says they were lucky.

"Everyone's coming by asking if we have gumbo yet or barbecue shrimp," Lemarie said. "Hopefully we'll be one of the first to reopen in Mid-City. Right now it's pretty barren." Lola's, Gabrielle restaurant, Fair Grinds Coffee House and CC's Coffee on Esplanade Avenue are all closed.

Lemarie said without the Fair Grounds it will be a struggle but he hopes the construction workers repairing the grandstand will ease the pain.

"Hopefully they'll make up for the trainers and jockeys and other track people," he said. There is little that can make up for what business owners on Carrollton Avenue between Esplanade Avenue and Canal Street experienced.

On this ravaged Mid-City stretch, the only signs of life are forklifts moving giant piles of garbage and debris. Sav-A-Center, Winn Dixie and Robert Fresh Market are dark and empty. Lil Ray's Diner looks like it got hit by rocket-propelled grenades.

At the corner of Fig Street and Carrollton Avenue, all that remains of two multistory homes are charred chimneys and black, wrought iron gates torched to a rusty orange. Dangerously close to the fire that took down these buildings is Ye Olde College Inn. Owner John Blancher said it flooded, then was looted and vandalized. It will take up to six months to reopen and Blancher said he is not sure there will be the customer base to support it.

"The College Inn is my greatest liability," he said.

Further down Carrollton Avenue, the Rock n' Bowl, Blancher's other business, escaped relatively unscathed and could reopen in two weeks. The only obstacles are the two stores downstairs.

"The Union Grocery underneath me is decaying," Blancher said. "It's been full of produce and meat since the storm, just rotting there and yet the landlord, Hibernia Bank, said it can't legally do anything about it."

There's also standing water in Blancher's downstairs party venue, Bowl Me Under, and mold is starting to grow up the walls, he said.

"How can I open when these things are rotting below me and my landlord won't do anything about it?"

Hibernia Bank officials did not return calls for comment.

Despite the difficulties, Blancher and Brooks do not intend to abandon their businesses or the Mid-City neighborhood.

"I have to try and bring them back, not only because they're my primary means of livelihood but because they're New Orleans institutions," Blancher said. "It's an obligation. Is it going to be easy? No, but the New Orleans diehards love these institutions and I know they'll come support them once they're up and running. They don't want to see them die anymore than I do."

* * * * * * * * * *

The echoes of Katrina are everywhere and show no signs of abating. It's a clearing-house for pain.

Drink motherfucker, drink!

Sink motherfucker, sink!

Can you think of three reasons to stay?

Think.

Yeah.

I'm too fucked up for the rest of the 49 states.

Perseverance is the purest fuck you.

And....ummm....excuse me.

My head's ringing.

I'm going to have to get this call.

"Hello? Lunacy? My darling. How I've missed you."

This town has been stripped down to its basest form, an amphibious city-state ripe for remolding into something.....something......wait.....I've lost it.

My mind, it comes and goes.

It happens a lot nowadays.

I'm not exactly right in the head.

And I can't say I give a damn.

Nowadays, I've come to realize there's no real damage in being delirious and insane. What the sober and sane see out their windows can't be any more unsettling than what I'm seeing out mine.

Except for that reflection, that strangely familiar face that I can't quite place, staring at me with those sad, hollow eyes and rained-on cheeks.

I can't tell if I hate him or pity him, or feel nothing at all.

It's too soon.

How much faith do we place in the architects of our future? What we are embarking on here in New Orleans is a complete refashioning of a major American metropolis. Enter the Ivy-league queers and cornershop intellectuals who heavily researched our quirky ways and culture by Googling "voodoo" and "hand grenades" and "swamps" and "murder capital of the world" and "tap-dancin' negro babies."

Yeah. They got us pegged. What grew organically over the course of three centuries will now be reproduced in five years by think tanks and congressional hearings run by coffin-fillers and closeted pedophiles insisting that the new architecture of New Orleans should resemble jungle gyms.

Hell, just ship 200,000 moon-bounces to New Orleans and let them set up shop wherever they like. And should they get hit by another hurricane, they'll all float to safety or out into the Gulf of Mexico, jumping for joy in their inflatable stupidity. Either way is good.

Before Katrina we had a population of roughly 500,000. Population estimates now hover around 80,000. Reasoning goes that we'll hit 250,000 before all is said and done.

The common refrain is that this is our chance to build a better city.

The common refrain is good riddance to those who don't return, i.e. the criminals, i.e. the poor, i.e. the blacks. At the same time, many lament the exodus of the people who gave us our culture, our music, the Mardi Gras Indians and second lines, those invisible souls who made New Orleans New Orleans.

And on both sides, we fall into the trap of categorizing the fallen according to our emotional needs.

Blacks as saviors.

Blacks as entertainment.

Blacks as an unwanted evil.

Welfare queens. Crackheads. Thieves. Rapists. Murderers.

Jazz musicians. Congo Square pioneers. Armstrong descendants.

Crippled stereotypes. Not people. Things to be dealt with and traded on the open market. Find a corner and stick-em in it. And be done with it. Move on to better things.

Revolutionary housing concepts. Blacks and whites living in peace. Poor and rich. Our pure and noble stab at paradise, an idyllic world of love where we all hold hands at that final moment when the fire-waves lose their course and veer straight into our bathrooms where we congregated for one last cleansing.

Raindrops on tear drops.
And sabers in kittens.
Bright blazing gunshots and
Bullets are hittin'
Strange wooden packages
Filled up with sin
These are a few of my favorite things

But it's too late for all of that. Take one step to the left and watch out for the corpse. She hasn't moved for a week and we're getting worried about her health. The blue skin don't mix well with the blackened toenails.
She hasn't smiled since her lungs filled with water.
Poor girl. We mourn her memory though it's hard to place her face and conjure her name.
Barbara. Betsy. Sally. Maybe Katie. Rhonda. Rachel. Chastain. Haley?
Doctor, I've gone crazy. Oh lady.
Something bad has happened to your insides from the outside and it's making us queasy.
I tasted her cracked and shriveled lips, but she gave nothing back.
And it hurts,
this heartbreak,
this taste of slow-growing crazy, that breaks just as quickly into
nothing at all.
And I sit in that nothingness trying to remember the taste of her dead lips.
But the memory won't come.
We've lost all sense of feeling.
So don't feel bad.
It's all good.
Except when it's bad.
And under those circumstances, we make nice with the bottle and she do treat us right.
And then we slip into oblivion and what comes next is what comes next is what comes next. And we wait for the moment to pass and pray that the other side is more palatable than what we see out our doors and windows and glasses and contacts and orbital bones. We pray the scene outside the glass is somehow different day to day. It's all we can do so we do it. We wait and it rains on the panes and it thunders and flashes angry electricity on blue rooftops that kick up nostalgic sparks.

Think of the 4th of July and roll with it.

We're that dying breed.

We're that close to something permanent.

But for now, I'm a hermit and that is a status damn near impossible to sustain when you ain't got no home and rely on the kindness of friends to provide a shack in the backyard in which to lay your head.

Someone mail me a battered tin cup.

I got me some beggin' to do.

Hey buddy, can you spare an affordable apartment and maybe some speed to keep me going? And a bottle of valium to bring me down? I ain't been sleeping much, you see? Can you? Because I can't. The booze done turned me blind. So how about a $10 bill? No? Fine. I'll just follow you home and see what we can work out.

Oh Christ.

Goddammit.

I tripped.

Hello blood.

A Circus Requiem

HOW WILL THEY REACT WHEN THEY SEE AN 87-YEAR OLD MAN VOMITING INTO THE WILLING MOUTH OF A TOPLESS CHEERLEADER SITTING ON THE FACE OF A 16-YEAR OLD HONOR STUDENT DRESSED LIKE AN UNCIRCUMCISED PENIS?

It's known as the Club to some, Ms. Mae's to others, a 24-hour haven for knockout artists and Ginger Men. It's a brightly lit pit of stupidity and sin popular among the old and
toothless, the young and privileged, and the pierced and proud.

Violence comes naturally in the mix.

On Sunday I grabbed a spot at the sparsely populated bar and ordered a Bud.

There were plenty of toothless old drunks and a few pierced punks, but the young and
privileged were nowhere to be found. Their numbers have been drastically reduced. Their
pretty little faces and collar-up pink Polo shirts parachuted to parts unknown. Our two
biggest colleges, the breeding pods, Loyola and Tulane, canceled their fall semesters. For
the stragglers that stayed behind, they confine their rare appearances to the weekends.

But come January, the doors will reopen and their numbers will grow. And for the glory
of we men, the sassy little nubile temptresses will flood our streets once again. But woe
be to us, they will come equipped with the metrosexual monsters of the Midwest looking
to make fantastic shadow figures on the walls. They will preen and primp and grind their
teeth on the rafters out of a profound frustration born from an inability to masturbate in
public.

In other words, the students return in January and trouble soon come.

That's straight from the mouth of the bartender serving me up beers at the Club. The
Colts/Bengals game was on the TV. Mariachi music blasted out of the juke. Latino laborers popped balls on the pool tables in the back.

"There's going to be trouble when the frat boys get back," the bartender said motioning
towards the Hispanic crew. "These people are out of control. They stole Ms. Mae's cell
phone the other night and that was the last straw for her. And it's not so much the Hispanic guys who have been here for awhile, it's the new guys who think they can do whatever
they want. So just wait until this place is filled with frat boys while the Mexicans are trying to get nasty with their girlfriends. You think there was trouble between the frat boys
and the punks? It's going to be a fucking full-on riot when the frat boys and Mexicans get
into it."

And so the bartender is pushing for a policy change at the Club. Let's call it the Mexican
Door Dance policy. Anybody who enters the Club must have an ID even if they look 100
years old. The idea is that most of these immigrant laborers do not have proper identification so, "No cerveza para tu."

58

"We'll also lock the back door so they can't sneak in."

Ahhh yes. How quickly many in New Orleans have adapted. From freely spitting words like "Goddamn those fucking niggers" to "I can't wait for these greasy wetbacks to float back to Mexico."

His fascinating geopolitical discourse was interrupted by a 21-year-old brunette wailing at a nearby table. I noticed her when she walked in. She was attractive but her neck propped up an oval psych ward. A fortyish, graying lawyer-type accompanied her, feeding her liquor and pills.

She took the first bottle and smashed it on the ground.

"Oh God no! Why?"

Turns out the fragile girl recently found out her cat died.

Turns out a coyote mauled her cat in New Mexico or wherever coyotes regularly feast on the long-tailed fuckers.

Ms. Mae, the wig-wearing, septuagenarian owner of the Club offered these consoling words.

"I'd like to slap that bitch into next week."

Death affects people differently in these post-Katrina days.

The girl eventually ran out of the bar, her frail arms wrapped tightly around her sides, sobbing quietly. The lawyer remained to drink another day, waiting for his shot at another post-pubescent conquest.

But who cares about all of that insignificant shit, right?

What do the happenings in some wretched barfly hangout mean in the grand scheme of things?

Perhaps you'd be more interested in hearing about a recent report in the Times-Picayune. Turns out that a family living in Lakeview, the ultra-swank hood abutting the breached 17th Street canal, called the Sewage and Water Board several months before Katrina to report that their backyard, which ran into the foot of the floodwalls, was under six inches of water. It was a common occurrence, they said. So how's about someone get their asses over here and check it out? Levee experts said this was more than a red flag; it was a fucking atomic bomb siren.

So what happened? Not a goddamn thing. The Water Board investigated and said indeed the water was coming from the canal but it failed to inform either the Levee Board or the Corps of Engineers. So this family's early warning system fell on deaf and doped-up ears. And as you know, the 17th Street floodwalls collapsed and Lakeview is no more.

An ensuing story detailed how our illustrious Levee Board spent no more than five hours every month or so inspecting hundreds of miles of levees, making sure they were done in time for lunch.

We were set up to die.

There's a quote in the paper today that said if the water topped the flood walls, instead of breaching them, we'd be almost back to normal by now. Instead, the flood walls were breached and about 80 percent of our city is a ghost town.

New Orleans didn't build these goddamn structures, the Corps did and the Corps is a federal agency and yet we are being called assholes and suicide cases for insisting on living in New Orleans.

So maybe it is our fault for believing the feds were capable of anything more than giving themselves pay raises and measuring their genitals with the mummified pinkies of the residents of the Ninth Ward.

Over the past five days there has been a theme running among the editorials of the Times-Picayune and its columnists. It goes something like this--the attention span of the feds for hurricane relief has expired. It is no longer a political necessity to come out in front of the cameras and weep and moan for the plight of New Orleans and promise relief and salvation.

We're yesterday's issue.

We're Velcro sneakers.

We ain't worth a monkey's tit.

And then the editorials go on to say, "How dare they," and, "Cities like Miami and L.A. better take note when Mother Nature levels their precious plastic whoredoms. Is this the best this country can do for one of its own cities?"

And make no mistake about it; New Orleans is in serious fucking trouble. The city is broke, the state is broke and we have no hurricane protection. Our police force is decimated, so much so that Mardi Gras has been slimmed down to eight days from 12. There is talk of flying in cops from around the country to help the NOPD patrol the parade routes, but that is an invitation to pistol whippings and plunger-rape.

Say what you want about our cops, and I've said it all as I believe my record will indicate, but during Mardi Gras they show amazing restraint when dealing with the hordes of chemical-induced loons. What do you think will happen if you throw in cops from Iowa or, God help us, Texas? How will they react when they see an 87-year-old man vomiting into the willing mouth of a topless cheerleader sitting on the face of a 16-year-old honor student dressed like an uncircumcised penis?

The National Guard is slowly slimming its ranks and without them we will all be at the mercy of the thin blue line. But oh those crazed camouflaged National Guardsmen would surely enjoy Mardi Gras. On one of their shift changes, the one night when those on the way out get to enjoy the special fruits of New Orleans, they packed the Balcony Bar, my unofficial home away from home, the place where I can drink $40 worth of booze and get charged no more than $6 because my best friends tend the taps and shot glasses.

They warned me to steer clear of the Balcony on this particular night and for some reason

I heeded on the side of caution.

It's going to get ugly, they said.

One of the bartenders spun the tale.

"I was scared for any girl that walked into the place," he said. "The National Guardsmen were a bunch of drooling, drunken assholes. One guy drank so much he was reduced to a zombie-state, walking around with spit swinging off of his lower lip. Guys were puking on the bar. Others passed out on the pool table. The Guard had a truck outside waiting to transport the worst of them to wherever they take blind-fucking drunk Guardsmen."

Corey, a burly former doorman, was unfortunate enough to be present for the degenerate scene while wearing a Batman t-shirt.

"One of these guys came up to me and called me a fag for wearing a Batman shirt. I nodded and said, 'Uh huh.' I knew better than to start shit with these guys. I throw one punch at one asshole and there would be 100 of them piled on top of me."

But as I said before, even though it is strange to be standing in line at the supermarket near a guy in cammies with an M-16 slung across his shoulder, the National Guardsmen are our guardian angels, protectors of the peace and the only thing standing between us and the meth-mad cops on a violence high.

We need them, and as their numbers dwindle, we step more gingerly around dark corners lest there be the low-brow, craggy face of a cop at the end of his rope eager to get it on with whatever life form comes within reach.

A few days after I returned in October two of the blue bastards threatened to break my camera and throw me in jail. I was interviewing a hippie collective that had set up shop in Washington Square in the Marigny providing medical care and cooking food for the nearby residents and anyone in need.

This display of kindness didn't sit well with some of the cops. They wanted everything under their control, they wanted to be feared or respected, both if possible.

So as I'm interviewing the head of the collective, two NOPD cops stroll in through the gates, slowly, with carefully choreographed bad-ass steps, hands on holsters, eyes hidden behind mirrored aviators.

The woman I was interviewing had warned me about them, that they had been by before making threats.

Get the fuck out or go to jail. Your choice.

As she engaged the pair in a heated discussion, I pulled out my camera and snapped off two pictures. The last shot shows the older cop with the pock-marked face pointing at me menacingly.

* * * * * * * * *

NOPD officers hide IDs while chasing off charity workers
By Richard A. Webster New Orleans CityBusiness Staff Writer

October 11, 2005 -- Two days after the New Orleans Police Department suspended three officers without pay for allegedly assaulting 64-year-old Robert Davis and an Associated Press cameraman on Bourbon Street, witnesses claim two NOPD officers threatened a charitable organization and a CityBusiness reporter.

NOPD public information officials were not immediately available to comment.

On Monday, a coalition of nonprofits and community groups officially opened Welcome Home New Orleans, a makeshift camp in Washington Square in Faubourg Marigny offering free medical care and hot meals.

Throughout the day, returning locals, city workers and members of the military poured into the park for plates of red beans and rice and cold drinks.

The New Orleans Jazz Vipers arrived at noon with their brass horns and guitars and resurrected the romping sounds of jazz long gone from this battered section of New Orleans.

Dee Anne Domnick, director of Barefoot Doctors' Academy, a Lacombe-based, nationwide network of midwives and medical professionals, was clearing dead branches and debris from the park when Rob Savoye, chief technology officer for the Barefoot Doctors' Academy, came running in her direction.

"They're trying to evict us," Savoye shouted. "They're trying to kick us out."

Two NOPD officers standing inside the park entrance had demanded to see a permit for use of the square.

Dr. Evangeline Franklin, chief of clinical services for the New Orleans Health Department, gave them verbal permission, Domnick said

When she asked the officers to identify themselves, the officers refused. When a CityBusiness reporter took two pictures of the confrontation, the officers ordered him to erase the photos.

Even after the reporter identified himself as a member of the press, the officers insisted he hand over his camera or risk arrest.

"We don't care what you're doing or who you're with," said the younger of the two. "You better erase those pictures of us now."

He then forcibly removed the reporter, who had refused to erase the photos, from the park.

"In a situation like this, where the whole system is topsy-turvy, you don't go insisting on permits when people are offering free health care and food in a disaster situation,"

Domnick said. "The (older) officer was trying to bully us and I thought my life was being threatened."

The badge number of the older officer was 1419, Savoye said.

Barefoot Doctors' Academy and the Rainbow Family of Living Light, a national coalition focused on community building and alternative lifestyles, arrived Thursday in New Orleans. The groups have provided free health care and food to thousands of people in Louisiana and Mississippi since hurricanes Katrina and Rita hit.

They use their own money, credit and donations. Everyone involved, including the medical professionals, is a volunteer.

Savoye said the groups mobilized when New Orleans Mayor C. Ray Nagin allowed residents to re-enter the city.

"We wanted to be here to welcome the locals back to the city," Savoye said. "There is a definite need for medical care and food and we'll be here as long as the need exists."

Domnick said she worked through every possible state and city agency to secure the rights to set up in Washington Square.

After contacting the New Orleans Emergency Operation Center she received a call from Dr. Sandra Robinson, deputy director of the New Orleans Department of Health, followed by a call from Franklin.

"I let (Franklin) know where I wanted to do it and she gave us permission to set up at Washington Square," Domnick said. "I asked if she had the authority to grant us permission and she said she did. I said we needed the gates unlocked and later that same day the gates were unlocked."

For the next five days, members of the Barefoot Doctors' Academy and the Rainbow Family cleared trash and debris, cutting and clearing dead branches from park trees.

"We've saved the city at least $5,000 in clean up costs," Domnick said.

The trouble started near 5 p.m. Sunday, when the older officer demanded to see a permit. Savoye said they had permission from the New Orleans Department of Health but the officer became irate.

"I could see this extreme kind of anger in him," Savoye said. "Any of these guys still on the job have to be maxed out so I'm trying to give him the benefit of the doubt but he was screaming at me and telling me to shut up."

Willow Kennedy, a Jackson Square musician who lives next to Washington Square, witnessed the initial confrontation.

"I saw the officer come up and get right in their faces," Kennedy said. "It was a pretty hot confrontation and he did the typical cop thing and said, 'You're leaving in 24 hours or you're going to jail.' That's what went down."

When the police arrived Monday the New Orleans Jazz Vipers cleared out, worried their instruments would be confiscated.

Outside the square, while the NOPD officers waited for a permit, Bill Moore, an international Teamsters Union representative based in Washington, D.C., sat next to a tractor trailer packed with donated water and orange juice to be delivered to the Barefoot Doctors' Academy.

"I've never been anywhere where a police officer would never even identify himself," Moore said.

"The older cop said they better give him the information he wanted because he had a gun. I don't think the younger cop liked that he was acting that way."

Once members of the Missouri National Guard arrived, led by Capt. Chris Moenster, the NOPD officers left within minutes.

"I don't think you'll see them again," Moenster said after speaking with the officers.

"They're overwhelmed and over-shocked. We're working with the police and it's been a good working relationship so far with very few conflicts."

Moenster said the officers were concerned about the debris piling on the sidewalks from the cleanup.

"From what I've seen, this place looks 100 percent better since the (Barefoot Doctors' Academy) got here," Moenster said. "People keep asking us where they can get a hot meal and now we're going to send everyone here."

Moore said the impact the Rainbow Family and Barefoot Doctors' Academy have had on Washington Square has been dramatic.

"Those people cleaned up that whole area and did a heck of a job," Moore said. "If this happened (in Washington D.C.) they would be giving these people accolades — not harassing them."

As the sun set, Felipe Chavez, a member of the Rainbow Family, lifted the barbecue lid and sprayed chicken pieces with water through a thick, savory smoke, preparing the evening's free meal. He took the day's events in stride.

"If they confronted us the right way without all of that intimidation attitude it would probably work out a lot better but instead they stick their chests out and say we're not supposed to be here," Chavez said. "They should be serving the people, not beating the people up. They shouldn't be in law enforcement if they can't control themselves."

* * * * * * * * * *

Lights out.

Draw the shades.

It's time to get nasty.

Now do you see what I'm saying about our need for the Guard?

It was a Norman Rockwell painting, two little brats in blue caught with slingshots in their pockets five feet away from a shattered picture-window, one kicking the dirt out of embarrassment, the other, the older cop, tightening his fists, curling his upper lip over his grinding teeth as the Major towered over both of them, calm, projecting power and reason.

It was the fucking food chain come to life.

Gangbangers beat on the citizens and the cops beat on the bangers and the citizens. Normally that's where the chain ended. But now, post-hurricane, the citizens, normally dead at the bottom, had the National Guardsmen to beat on the cops.

And these two officers were exposed for who they were, low-rent criminals.

In these post-Katrina days there are more dark corners in New Orleans than lighted bars and willing whores.

Now that daylight savings is in effect, by the time I drive home from work the sun has set. I take Vets to Fleur de Lis to Carrollton to Fountainbleu to Napoleon. These once thriving streets have been abandoned. It is apparent during the day, but at night the imprint of Katrina is felt in your bones. A total blackout, but unlike any blackout previously experienced. The total absence of light is overshadowed by the complete void of human life. It is something more than death; it is as if life never touched these areas. Grand, stately homes appear to be relics of a lost civilization.

Shattered windows and broken-down doors. The mean brown waterlines tattooed on the stucco and siding. Not one waterline per house, but at least five for every terrible rise in depth. Two feet. Then three feet. It sits for a few hours, makes its mark then rises another four feet.

I make my way down Fountainbleu and down each street it's more of the same.

Cold blackness. Silence save for the random car creeping and searching for the first sign of life and civilization.

These were once the neighborhoods where I drank beer with friends at Labor Day barbecues. These were the neighborhoods I enjoyed long talks with strangers while slurping down crawfish meat over newspaper-covered tables.

And it's all gone.

Several out-of-town friends, after reading these demented words of mine, have written back, shocked at how I describe the current state of New Orleans. Apparently, much of the nation is under the false impression that New Orleans is creeping back to normal, that it is business as usual.

Let me paint as clear a picture as possible.

Before Katrina we had a population of just under 500,000. Estimates today put our population at 75,000 and maybe half of that is comprised of out-of-town workers.

There is only a small slip of habitable land. It runs from Uptown through the Central

Business District, French Quarter, Faubourg Marigny and the Bywater. The rest of the city is demolished. New Orleans East, the Ninth Ward, Lakeview, Mid-City and Gentilly. A curfew remains in place. The few grocery stores that are open close at 8 p.m., at the latest. There are thousands of people desperate to return but they have no place to live, and FEMA is not distributing the long-promised trailers.

And then there are the diehards.

I got a tip from Brent who works for a national advocacy group on homelessness that there was a group of elderly men living in a small pocket of New Orleans East in apartments that just a few weeks ago were under five feet of water.

* * * * * * * * * *

Diehards rough it in moldy conditions
By Richard A. Webster New Orleans CityBusiness Staff Writer

January 30, 2006 -- In the vast wasteland that is eastern New Orleans — mile after mile of industrial wreckage, blown-out storefronts and abandoned homes — a small group of elderly men live alone in flood-damaged apartments off Chef Menteur Highway.

They sleep on filthy, blackened mattresses that once were submerged in more than 5 feet of polluted water.

Their apartments stink of mold that has grown unchecked for nearly five months behind walls and under warped, rolling floorboards.

They are living at the bottom of a recently drained lake and have lived in these wretched conditions since Hurricane Katrina wrapped her outer bands around New Orleans.

They are old, sick and alone. And in many of the most battered sections of the city, they represent the permanent population — the poor souls who remained throughout the storm and the tortuous aftermath because they had no other options.

They have limited contact with the outside world, depending on volunteer groups and the Red Cross to bring them food and medical supplies. They exist in an environment that lacks basic services found in even the most poverty-stricken communities such as electricity, gas and working phone lines. Sitting in his closet of an apartment, underneath exposed beams once hidden by a ceiling that long since collapsed, Bobby Rideau, 66, said he had no choice but to stick it out.

"I wasn't going to stick myself in no Superdome," Rideau said. "That trouble in there was the worst and I would have been in the middle of it as a senior citizen, you know? I was safer here if you think about it."

Clyde Brumfield, 54, is Rideau's neighbor. He is a diabetic, suffers from high blood pressure and depends on eight different medicines to get through the day. Despite his failing health, Brumfield never left his apartment, which now reeks of festering mold.

"I woke up in bed and there was water everywhere," Brumfield said as he shuffled through his one-bedroom apartment, pointing to the buckled floor, warped doorways and thick layers of mud under his sink.

"There were dead bodies all up through here," he said. "This is a disaster area just like the Ninth Ward. Two people down the street had everything in life you could want. First the woman died and then the man died. Their kids came back and put everything in the dump. They only took the pictures. They didn't want to stay and I don't blame them. But God has fixed it for me that I'm still living and that's the best I can do. The only thing I'm missing is my brother Noland."

Since the storm broke, Brumfield hasn't been able to locate his older brother, Noland, who lived at 12941 Parlage St.

Rideau and Brumfield are retired and live off government assistance.

When Brandon Darby, director of the nonprofit activist group Ninth Ward Common Ground, heard about Rideau and Brumfield, he and a team of volunteers brought food and water and took them to the nearest pharmacy for medicine. Darby said their situation is not unique.

"There are hundreds of people I interact with who are in the same situation, some much worse," Darby said. "Elderly people staying in moldy houses and still getting rained on but they don't want any government contact. They're freaked out so they hide in their homes while different individuals bring them water and food sporadically. And that's how we find out about them. People will call and say, 'There's this elderly person I've been taking care of for the past three months but I have to go back to my job, life or kids.'"

Darby said he has identified 14 individuals in the ravaged Lower Ninth Ward who never left and now live in utter squalor.

Life in eastern New Orleans is not easy, Rideau said.

He hitchhikes from Chef Menteur Highway to the Sav-A-Center on Tchoupitoulas Street for groceries, many times on the back of a pickup. Other days he depends on the sporadic appearances by the Red Cross meal van.

"I'd stand on the corner trying to get water and ice and then they'd come and see we were all back here," Rideau said. "Without me going out there no one would know we were here."

Before Katrina, eastern New Orleans was populated by more than 100,000 residents. Now, roughly 1,000 families call it home, according to estimates from the office of City Councilwoman Cynthia Willard-Lewis.

Four feet of water inundated Rideau's apartment. This day, the walls are marked with mustard yellow streaks from the previous morning's rain that poured in from the *cavernous black hole in the ceiling.*

His mattress is stained from mold and mud. On the opposing wall hang hernia straps he has worn since 1996.

Shortly after the storm Rideau said he became violently sick and couldn't hold down any food. It got so bad the National Guard took him to Ochsner Hospital, where he stayed for eight days as doctors drained tank after tank of gray liquid from his stomach, the by-product of living in closed quarters breathing in dust and mold. After yet another hernia operation, he returned to his cave of an apartment.

"The military did everything they could to get us out of here but I kept telling them I wasn't ready yet, more work to do, more cleaning up, more this, more that," Rideau said. "I stood them off and finally they got tired of trying. If I left, the looters would have picked this place as clean as a Christmas turkey."

Now Rideau spends much of his time standing on the side of Chef Menteur Highway with a sign asking for help to find a place to park his long-promised but never-delivered FEMA trailer.

The sign reads: "Need a safe spot to park a trailer near this location. Driveway will work. Local boy needs your help."

* * * * * * * * *

There is an awful sense that we are yesterday's news. That all of those oh-so-sincere pledges to rebuild New Orleans were politically inspired in the wretched aftermath of it all.

While touring the remains of a Lakeview home that the floodwaters transformed into something resembling a Grand Central Station bathroom, Alaskan Senator Ted Stevens, with all the sensitivity of a cobra, asked the devastated couple who called the house home for years, "Why would you want to rebuild this?"

A spokesman for Stevens said his words were taken out of context.

I pray every night that a bull-moose mounts Stevens in the cold crystal drifts of Alaska, slamming its heavy hooves into his shoulder blades as it pumps its icy shaft deep into his small intestine, rupturing the entirety of his vital organs bringing on a swift, animalistic, sex-kick death so Satan can get on with Stevens' long-destined date in the iron maiden.

I offer this quote for worldwide dissemination. Use it in whatever context you wish.

It is my loving invocation to the gods. Or God. Whatever rocks your soul.

But to be fair, there is also a faction of our local politicians more interested in protecting political turf and cronies than in protecting the people of New Orleans. Sen. Walter Boasso proposed a bill that would consolidate local levee boards, the groups in charge of flood protection, into a statewide board that would rid the disparate organizations of

68

political appointees (Mike Brown-type motherfuckers) and replace them with flood control professionals and experts (i.e. James Lee Witt). Several politicians successfully killed the bill despite the fact that a massive group of displaced business leaders said if the current levee board system remained in place they would think hard about ever returning to New Orleans.

Rep. Ken Odinet from St. Bernard, a parish almost completely wiped out by the floods, said he wanted local control of levee boards to remain in place because it is best equipped to provide the best protection.

Public outrage ensued. The Times-Picayune listed all of the fuckers who voted against this bill, beseeching the public to email and call them to express their rage.

Lt. Gov. Mitch Landrieu said he would bring the issue up again in a special session in January.

Our spineless Governor Blanco has remained silent on the issue and many suspect she encouraged the defeat of the bill in favor of her own proposal that would simply create a state oversight board of the levee boards, another pointless layer of bureaucracy.

This is probably boring insider shit but it is one of the most important issues facing the city as it illustrates how our elected leaders are unable to abandon their self-serving interests.

Despite more than 1,000 deaths and the near complete destruction of our city, for the politicians it is business as usual.

But that's not what y'all wanted to hear from me, right?

Get on with the fractured, drug-sodden ramblings.

Ok.

Here goes.

I'm not patient. I'm inherently incoherent and patently pissed-off to the point where I pray for the moose-raping of my enemies. And make no mistake, we here in New Orleans are cultivating a long list of enemies who best steer clear of our watery ways. We have mutated into web-footed, man-frogs with poisonous pores that heave heavy in the Southern heat creating our own toxic sweat-floods. And we're bottling the shit for future use. "Oh those booze-crazy, bar-humping slugs of New Orleans are so funny with their weird talk and drooling threats," the people say. "Let's give them a cursory listen before they slump over their gin and tonics, arms wrapped around dreams dying on the bar that has bared witness to so many of their lonely proclamations of hope and future intentions of greatness.

They're so funny and special and quaint. Nail some bottle caps to their feet and watch them tap that dance that echoes throughout the Quarter corridors and draws tourists to snap pictures and toss dimes in cardboard boxes."

But we're fucking clowns no more.

To be sure, there remains a majority of apolitical people content to sit out the battle. It's messy and political talk is so unsavory. There will always be the dead weight, cow-dumb masses that will never get it.

Wherever you are, look to your left or right and you too will see that the members of this useless herd are rife within your own community.

But there is hope in New Orleans driven by a growing rage. Among the people who have chosen to make a stand on the driftwood we call sidewalks, there is a growing sense of abandonment by our supposed leaders. Eyes have been opened.

In many corners once devoid of political activism, there is talk of protests. And for those who are not inclined to such overt political activity, just being here, keeping their businesses open, and defying those who say New Orleans is a death pool, a statement is being made.

I recently ran into Jules at Sav-A-Center, a local supermarket. He is the son of the famed beat poet Robert Stockton. He is a tough bastard, a fortyish skeletal punk rocker and Mardi Gras float builder. As tough as he is, he told me he has broken down several times since Katrina made landfall, as we all have.

The only thing he managed to save from his ruined home were the precious books of his long-gone, revered father.

We are all operating on the extreme edges of human emotion. Tears come easily.

We shared our evacuation stories and then shared our devotion to New Orleans.

"I'll never leave," Jules said. "We're going to bring this city back and make sure it is as fucked-up and unique as ever. Like it's always been. This is our home and no one is going to take it from us."

It seems as if the powers-that-be would rather we abandon New Orleans to free them from the responsibility of rebuilding and spending billions to do so. But we refuse because our continued presence here is the greatest single protest in modern history. And this protest can be found in some of the most devastated areas like Plaquemines and St. Bernard parishes where small clans have returned despite a complete lack of basic human services.

Fallen Empire

By Richard A. Webster New Orleans CityBusiness Staff Writer

November 14, 2005 -- Two miles north of Port Sulphur, Hurricane Katrina made herself known.

The once-green grounds are now a lifeless brown. Boat carcasses lie scattered along the highway. A roof without a house rests in scarred trees leaving cinderblock foundations below with nothing to support.

"It gets worse," said Venice fisherman Acy Cooper while riding in a Louisiana Seafood Board caravan of politicians, seafood industry officials and fishermen touring what is left of the Plaquemines Parish fishing community.

Unlike Lakeview or the Ninth Ward, no water-marks line the houses. What remains of the homes of Empire can be seen in the trees: a piece of a wall wrapped around a trunk or a door held up by a heavy branch next to a rocking chair hanging on a web of twigs.

On one muddy lot, a short flight of pale-green stairs leads to a small porch and nothing beyond.

The bus crawls to a stop at the Empire Shipyard, once the second-largest commercial landing for seafood in the United States.

An Empire fisherman jumps off the bus and walks down the canal, past piles of boats scattered like matchsticks.

"The kingdom of heaven is Empire," he shouts.

Immediate assistance is needed for the fishermen who called Port Sulphur, Empire, Buras and Venice home, said A.J. Fabre, president of the Louisiana Shrimp Association

"We were already on our death bed before the hurricane," he said. "We were getting killed by imported product and a drop in the price we get for our shrimp. We've always been the low man on the totem pole and if we don't get help now it will be the death blow."

Plaquemines Parish suffered the full rage of a Category 4 hurricane--a 35-foot storm surge backed by 150-mph winds blasted ashore and laid waste to everything in its path. Only three people lost their lives but most of those who survived came through the other side with only the clothes on their backs.

The fishing infrastructure has been devastated, said Harlon Pearce, owner of LA Fish in Kenner.

"One blessing from a storm like this is that it brings more fish," said Pearce. "We're loaded with product but we don't have the labor force, infrastructure, gear, equipment or

boats to get out and do our jobs."

Waterways are crammed with collapsed boats, refrigerators and other debris making navigation next to impossible. Utility pipelines for natural gas, electricity and fuel no longer exist. All refrigeration equipment is gone and ice is a rarity.

"It's just 30 miles of destruction," said Gregory Holt, president of Daybrook Fisheries Inc. in Empire. "Thirteen-thousand people used to live between Port Sulphur and Venice and now there's nobody."

Holt looked out the window as the bus stopped outside Empire. Hurricane Katrina lifted one of Daybrook's $7-million, multi-ton vessels and dropped it in the middle of Highway 23. A second Daybrook ship lay just a few hundred yards away.

Holt said it will cost $1.2 million to remove each vessel.

Daybrook employed 270 people before the storm and planned to expand to 330. Now it is tasked with the surreal job of rolling their massive ships off the highway and repairing its facilities that disappeared under the black waters when the storm broke.

"We're trying to rebuild but you can't rebuild a business without a community," Holt said. "Look at it out there. There's nothing left — the schools, houses, churches, everything is gone. But these people have to come back."

Holt said Daybrook will invest more than $36 million to help with reconstruction.

Before Hurricane Katrina there were between 12,000 and 15,000 licensed commercial fishermen in Louisiana. Pearce predicts only half will return. "Fishermen don't have money saved up and most don't have insurance because it's too expensive," Pearce said.

"People will lose businesses that have been built up over 30 years. But I think the true fishermen will survive because it's in their hearts. We'll probably lose a lot of the weekend warriors."

Peter Gerica used to live in a solid brick house near eastern New Orleans and trawled for shrimp and crab in lakes Pontchartrain and Borgne.

Gerica decided to tough out Hurricane Katrina after he was told it would be similar to Hurricane Camille.

"They said it would have a 24-foot surge like Camille and I went through Camille so that meant about 3 inches of water under the house," Gerica said. "The National Guard told me they wanted me to leave and I said, 'Kiss my ass. I'm staying.'"

Three other families in Gerica's neighborhood chose to stay, including the Rev. Arthur "Red" Ginart at St. Nicholas of Myra Church.

"He said he didn't want to evacuate, that it would be God's will if he died," Gerica said. "So I guess it was God's will. The church was all blown apart except for two large statues at the foot of the altar."

Soon after Hurricane Katrina smashed into his house, Gerica knew he made a terrible and possibly deadly mistake. The house went down sometime after 8 a.m. Aug. 29.

Gerica found himself in the middle of the street with his 77-year-old mother in 4 feet of water rising another 4 feet every 10 minutes, he said. Then came the tornadoes.

"No one wants to talk about it but I know there were tornadoes because there was hail and it don't hail during a hurricane," Gerica said.

As he was tying his mother, daughter and dog to a nearby tree, Gerica's wife floated by on a door.

"She told me to take care of our daughter and then she was gone," Gerica said. "I didn't know if she was alive, dead or otherwise."

After seven hours in the tree, Gerica managed to get his family into a friend's boat. He climbed the rigging, spotted his wife trapped on debris and pulled her to safety.

Gerica said he told his story while on the Plaquemines tour bus because he didn't want people to forget the fishermen in Orleans Parish who suffered the same crippling blows.

"The only thing I saved is a 24-foot boat," Gerica said. "Everything else I worked for my entire life is gone, just like every other fisherman. We're living off of my little girl's college fund now. She's only got one year left and hopefully I can replace it. Katrina wasn't prejudiced about what she took or where she took it. She took everything."

* * * * * * * * * *

We live in the ruins.

We drink in the ruins.

We fight and scream and love in the ruins.

In the shadow of old New Orleans, friends reconnect and lovers embrace.

In the shadow of old New Orleans, dying relationships do what dying relationships do. They die.

In the shadow of old New Orleans, we worship the memory of old New Orleans.

Old New Orleans tortured us and beat us down and drove us to flee in wild-eyed terror.

But she always pulled back us back, we the fortunate fools whose souls could never shake that boiling, rolling, rockin' spirit that attracted us from day one.

Like junkies, like lushes, like whores and obsessive parents, we cradle our precious city and feed it bottle caps of Absinthe when it hurts.

Our secret addiction.

Our public compulsion.

Turn your backs on us.

We'd rather you didn't but we always preferred to be left alone.

So be it.

Talk of secession has entered the public square.

Saudi Acadiana.

But we know we are not alone. There are people out there born with that wretchedly wonderful scarlet fleur de lis, the mark of the beast, the cherished insanity of New Orleans. And so long as they are kicking, the survivors of New Orleans will never be alone or longing for allies on
the outside.

And I like to watch cats mix sexually with dogs.

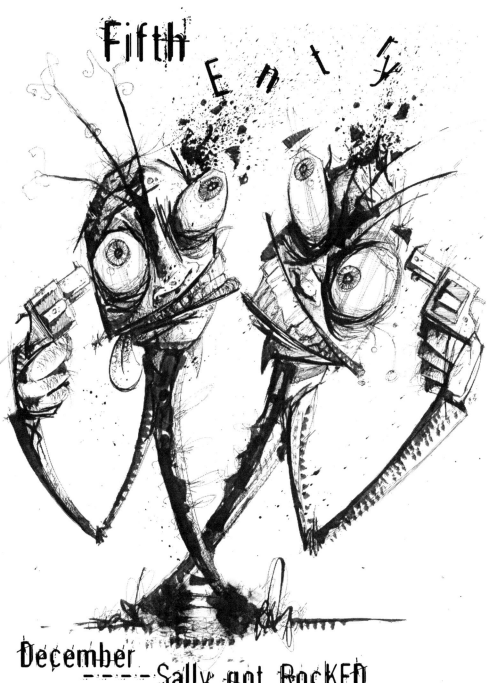

Fifth Entry

December 7 2005

Sally got RocKED

THE KEYS OF MY COMPUTER ARE NOW THICK
WITH THE BLOOD THAT HAS BEEN POURING OUT

OF MY NOSE EVER SINCE YOUR WRETCHED NAME
ENTERED THE EQUATION. I NEED A MOMENT TO
REST, TO REGROUP AND TEMPER THE

POND-SKIPPING BEAT OF MY RAGING HEART.

TOO LATE.

It's been three months since the floodwaters receded and yet the city still bears the water-mark tattoos of Katrina--the levees broken and battered, large swaths of dead neighbor-hoods left without power and people while the politicians are stuck on stupid.

But slowly the citizenry is taking up arms, organizing and writing letters to their congres-sional leaders. I won't pretend this is a large movement, but in small corners noise is being made and that is a start.

People are beginning to demand an end to corruption and cronyism and patronage. Whether it will have an impact remains to be seen.

In today's Times-Picayune, local columnist Chris Rose wrote how Katrina continues to kill in the way of suicides brought on by uncontrollable despair. He told the story of a young couple that returned to the city--the wife, a native, wanting to stay, the husband ve-hemently against remaining. With nothing going right, and the booze flowing, they made a Romeo and Juliet blood pact. The young wife thought they were joking. The husband did not and killed himself.

Experts say that after catastrophes suicide is not uncommon. That's where we're at. Where y'at?

It's a common saying like, "How ya doin'?"

For some, the answer is, "Terrible. Do you have a gun?"

Not yet, for there is still hope.

Despite my terrible descriptions of this city, I believe hope remains, as do my friends who have chosen to stake their claim. If hope didn't exist I wouldn't be here.

Well, that's not true. I like living in a doomed city. I like the idea of existing in a place forsaken by the rest of the country.

And it's true, we have been forsaken. Ask yourself when was the last time you read a comprehensive report about the state of New Orleans. Is it even on the radar of your lo-cal media? Save for a few paragraphs on page 16 or a 10-second piece on the local news showing drunks on Bourbon Street, when did you last get any real news from my home? Do you actually know what's going on? If it weren't for my demented words would you have a clue?

Of course not. We're yesterday's news. It's a point I've berated and will continue to be-rate because the national media won't do it.

Hundreds of thousands of New Orleanians remain stranded across the country waiting to be told that it's time to come home, that it's safe.

If I can ask anything of you, my friends and fellow degenerates and political assassins, it would be to contact your representatives and demand that they do not forget about the tortured souls who remain here in New Orleans.

That's all.

That's everything.

Except for this--put yourselves in our position. Take a moment to look around when you walk or drive to work. Imagine every house abandoned, windows blown out, red-death marks scrawled on front doors. Think of the corner grocery store you frequent resembling the bombed-out relics of Managua. Imagine that every conversation you have with friends or strangers includes talk of loss, death, violence and predictions of ruin and rage. "Have you been to the Ninth Ward yet? New Orleans East? Lakeview? Have you seen the complete and total annihilation of St. Bernard?"

As a writer, I understand tragedy is sexy. But don't mistake these words of mine as exaggerations.

Unfortunately, as a journalist, I understand the life-cycle of a story.

A girl gets hit by a car. She survives, miraculously. Her story is written and readers cry over her pain. Weep for her unfortunate plight. The article ends with a paragraph of vague hope. She's trying to pull through. Her strength is being put to the test. The end.

No follow-up.

Nothing.

Months pass and the paper moves on to political corruption and national shame and pastry chefs who have perfected the art of double-layered Gemini cakes favored by Jessica Simpson but actively opposed by Condoleezza Rice who may or may not run for president which may coincide with the suspected and prayed for nuptials of Brad Pitt and Angelina Jolie who are thinking of adopting a kid from Darfur or maybe Trenton or Gary, Indiana.

Did you hear that Rubik's Cube is making a comeback?

How about the new sitcom starring Al Sharpton?

Are you going to vote in the upcoming local elections pitting Ms. Mary God-Whore vs. Johnny Do-Like-A Little-Porn?

Death-spreading chickens and rabid sows making love like Marilyn Chambers and John Holmes.

Furbees and X-Boxes and the FCC regulating cable TV and PBS under fire.

But what about that chick who….ummm...that girl who got hit, or was it gored, by a….. was it a Mitsubishi?

What the hell happened to that girl who was on the news the other day? Last week? What was her name?

Was she bulimic? Crossbred and squeamish?

After all this time, who really gives a fuck what happened to her? She's probably fine. If not, we would have heard about it on the news, right?

Right?

No. She died. Her doctor hit the morphine a little heavy one night and he turned the late shift into his own private Idaho and turned her gurney into a laboratory for skull fractions by way of skull-fucking and she choked on a penile-shaped stethoscope.

The hospital board ruled her death to be a product of bad dreams and night tremors.

Didn't you hear about it? It was all over the news. Two years after the first story.

What? Did you forget about her? Did you think it was all going to turn out like Strawberry Shortcake and Iraq?

Don't be stupid.

She never stood a chance.

But it's all Doris Day and Tom Cruise.

A yellow Trivial Pursuit wedge.

Stash it under your pillow and hope this little bit of knowledge mutates into a quarter or at least a flawed nickel you can sell to the bald coin dealer down the street with the wildly flapping man-boobies that the local kids masturbate to in the adjacent gas station bathroom where we were all conceived.

It's all so ugly.

And somewhere in all that ugliness I had a point, but the beer do get me loopy.

Now excuse me while I head out into the great new New Orleans night. It's time to strap on my night-vision goggles that make everything look like St. Patrick's Day, so I can properly monitor the doings and goings-on of formerly domesticated animals turned truck-fucking AIDS monkeys.

You never know when they're finally going to make their move.

Mental health neglected post-Katrina
By Richard A. Webster New Orleans CityBusiness Staff Writer

April 18, 2006 -- Dale Evans, a 51-year-old paranoid schizophrenic prone to violent outbursts, arrived in Conway, Ark., shortly after Hurricane Katrina on a bus packed with New Orleans evacuees.

He was disoriented, his feet covered in open sores. Evans held a small paper bag in his battered hands containing medicine and a piece of paper with the name and number of Pamela LeBan, proprietor of the Ray of Hope group home where Evans resided before the storm.

Lou Strain, director of Counseling Associates in Conway, said more than 1,000 people from New Orleans arrived after the hurricane and several had serious mental health conditions.

"We had some people actively hallucinating," Strain said. "They were suicidal, homicidal and gravely disabled and they were mixed in with everyone else, including children. We could tell they were off their medication because they were hearing and seeing things."

Evans was the most serious case, said Jackie Fliss, executive director of Independent Living Services in Conway.

"I was astounded that with his disability he was doing as well as he was, and he was not doing well," Fliss said. "He was in bad shape."

Evans' sister, Jean Murphy, said her family thought LeBan had a hurricane evacuation plan.

As it turns out, Murphy claims the "evacuation plan" called for Evans to be "dumped off" at the Louisiana Superdome with a bag of medicine, a note and no identification. Murphy said her initial anger has given way to relief. She said Evans is doing better than ever in Conway now that he is finally free of the Louisiana mental health care system.

"The blessing of Katrina is that the program he's in now is 50 times better than anything the state of Louisiana had and we've been dealing with the state system for at least 25 years," said Murphy.

LeBan denied "dumping" anyone and said she personally accompanied Evans and the three other men under her care inside the Superdome. But as the building swelled with people and the chaos mounted, LeBan said it became impossible to keep track of four adult individuals with severe mental disabilities.

"They were bouncing off the walls," LeBan said. "It was too much for them to take being around all of those people. I wanted to be with my clients but I also didn't want to leave my family. Eventually we got separated and I lost track of all of them. It was terrible."

In the wake of Katrina, the Louisiana mental health care system is in tatters. Only 11 of 23 New Orleans-area mental health care clinics are open, including just six of 16 in the city.

Ninety-seven mental health care beds were lost when the state shut down Charity Hospital and only 24 beds have been replaced at surrounding facilities.

In the November special legislative session, lawmakers cut the budget for mental health care from $263 million to $243 million.

Dr. Fred Cerise, secretary of the Louisiana Department of Health and Hospitals, said it's a dangerous time to cut clinic funding.

"The need for mental health care in a post-disaster situation typically peaks six to nine months after the event," Cerise said. "Unfortunately for people with chronic mental illness, they've had their delivery systems disrupted and we need to find a way to recreate that."

Yakima Black, executive director of the Louisiana Mental Health Association in Baton Rouge, said the lack of mental health clinics was a problem before the storm. It gave rise to the unlicensed "board and care" group homes such as the one operated by LeBan.

"These types of group homes are not licensed by DHH. They're licensed by the same people who make sure restaurants are sanitary," Black said. "Anyone can operate one. They provide food and shelter and that's it. So many people with severe mental illnesses are being taken advantage of but, because there are a limited number of mental rehab facilities, these group homes flourish. The problem is pervasive."

Since being diagnosed as a schizophrenic 30 years ago, Evans lived in various group homes and never received proper care, said his mother, Charlye Inbau.

At one point he was under the supervision of Dr. Maria Carmen Palazzo, recently indicted by a federal grand jury for 17 counts of health care fraud. She faces up to 62 years in prison and fines of up to $4.2 million. Evans' sister, Robyn Schuler, said Palazzo charged Medicaid more than $10,000 a month to care for Evans.

"She was charging for family therapy when none of us had ever been to a therapy session, and for day care, which was them basically sitting him in front of a TV," Schuler said. "My mother eventually called the Medicaid fraud hotline on her."

Prior to Katrina, Evans lived in LeBan's group home on Jumonville Street with three other men — all suffering from various forms of schizophrenia, bipolar disorder and paranoia.

Schuler said it was all they could afford and placing Evans in a private institution was financially out of the question.

When Hurricane Katrina menaced the Gulf Coast, LeBan said her only evacuation option was the Superdome.

"I never thought about getting completely out of the city," LeBan said. "I was going to evacuate them to a shelter because I never thought the city would flood like it did. I thought we'd be back in the group home in a day or two. I gave them each pill boxes with a week's worth of medicine but I couldn't keep track of them all."

Strain said she was shocked to hear someone would take a person with paranoid schizophrenia to the Superdome.

"We have residential care for the chronically medical ill and of course we have an evacuation plan," said Strain. "If we did something like that, dropping people off at a shelter, we'd be sued and shut down."

Independent Living Services in Conway provides Evans with computer and employment training and art music classes. Murphy said her brother is so comfortable in his new surroundings that when they came to visit him after Christmas he went "ballistic."

"We were going to take him out to dinner but he freaked because he thought we were going to take him back to New Orleans," Murphy said. "They had to explain that he was going to stay in Arkansas. I don't know what he experienced at the Superdome but I'm sure it wasn't pleasant."

Evans recently won a walking competition in the Arkansas Special Olympics. In typical New Orleans fashion, Fliss said he completed the entire race with his hands in his pockets.

"It was more of a stroll than a walk," she said.

LeBan, now living in Shreveport, said she is anxious to return to New Orleans and rebuild her group home. She said she will try to retrieve her former clients.

* * * * * * * * *

Fifth Entry Part II
Circa December 14, 2005
Momma, Sally Don't Look So Good

A report in the Times-Picayune detailed yet another suspected suicide, this time at Chris Owens' nightclub. Chris Owens is a woman in the shape of a drag queen in the shape of a man who is really a woman who wants to be something in-between.

Anyway, this past Sunday night a man popped himself in the head in a booth and slumped over in his own viscous puddle of glop and former life cells.

It's not an epidemic yet, but the stories are jarring.

Before Katrina, suicides in the news were unrelated, the products of isolated sadness and misery--those who couldn't cope or tried to reach for something greater than they were capable, who found themselves in a dark place with no happy memories. Or maybe insanity clouded those happy memories, twisting them into something mean and unbearable.

But in post-Katrina New Orleans, we are all tempted by the great truth of the noose.

* * * * * * * * * *

NO suicides double after Katrina
By Richard A. Webster New Orleans CityBusiness Staff Writer

March 13, 2006 -- Since Hurricane Katrina there have been several high-profile and highly publicized suicides by New Orleans residents and evacuees.

Dr. James Kent Treadway, 58, killed himself Nov. 16 in his Uptown house.

One month later, local filmmaker Stevenson Palfi, 53, shot himself in his Mid-City home after the floodwaters washed away his life's work.

Days earlier, an unidentified man sat on a couch next to the bathroom inside the Chris Owens club on Bourbon Street and as people danced around him he took out a handgun and ended his life.

Finally, in late January aspiring New Orleans rapper Jerome "Slim Rome" Spears, 28, killed his fiancée, Rachel Harris, in a rented home in Atlanta and shot her 4-year old son

82

in the back of the head before turning the gun on himself.

On Jan. 27 newspapers across the country picked up an Associated Press story with the headline, "Stress after Katrina 'recipe for suicide.'"

But has this proven to be the case? Experts say while the suicide rate has increased in the immediate aftermath of the storm, the worst may be yet to come.

"The idea that things are not returning to normal, that reality is beginning to set in," said Norma Rutledge, executive director of the Baton Rouge Crisis Intervention Center. "We say this isn't a sprint, it's a marathon, and that idea of what a marathon is is beginning to take on real proportion when it comes to trying to recover and that's draining every bit of resources people have, including emotional resources and the coping skills, the things that have served people well over time. It's all beginning to wear thin and that brings us to a dangerous point."

In the first four months following the hurricane, at a time when the city's population was less than 100,000, seven people in New Orleans killed themselves, according to the coroner's office. If this trend played out over the course of an entire year 21 people per 100,000 could be expected to commit suicide, approximately double the amount in 2004 when the New Orleans rate was nine suicides per 100,000.

While it represents an increase, experts say the true explosion may lie six months down the road.

"What I've seen are a lot more people developing anxiety disorders which follows chronic stress," said Dr. Douglas Greve, a psychiatrist with a private practice in the French Quarter. "People are coming in with tremors and nervousness and can't sleep, people who've lost everything and haven't been able to return to their lives. We can tolerate stress for a period of time but then it starts to get worse and slowly develops into serious depression. I think there will be more suicides in the next six months but right now it's a lot of anxiety."

Marguerite Redwine, CEO of Via Link in New Orleans, a crisis hotline, said severe depression is on the rise. Before the storm they averaged two to three calls a day from people who displayed significant signs of despair and suicidal tendencies. After the storm that number has risen to approximately 14.

"The people we're getting now have never interfaced with the mental health system before but now are feeling depressed and lost because of what they're confronted with," Redwine said. "People feel like they can't go on because they don't know how they can ever recover from the devastating losses."

According to the Baton Rouge Crisis Intervention Center, the number of calls fielded on the statewide suicide crisis line jumped from nine in January 2005 to 246 in September, 272 in October, 244 in November, 213 in December, and 230 in January 2006.

Dr. Frank Campbell, executive director of the office of clinical research with the Baton

Rouge Crisis Intervention Center, said typically 85 percent of people exposed to a traumatic event recover in a year but expects that number to be significantly lower for the survivors of Katrina.

"If you were a rape victim you wouldn't necessarily lose all of your built-in resources like your home and family, neighbors, friends, etc.," said Campbell. "We're dealing with something we've never faced before. We don't have a history of people experiencing repeated anxiety issues like this to know where their breaking point might be."

Mack Moore, assistant director for the suicide prevention and confidential crisis helpline in Pensacola, Fla., an area hard hit by Hurricane Ivan in 2005, said immediately following a catastrophic event, people tend to focus on survival needs such as food and shelter. After those needs have been met and the months creep by, people are forced to realize they may never recapture their old lives.

Six months after Katrina, many people in New Orleans hold onto the hope that they might be able to return home but eventually banks will foreclose on homes, jobs will be lost and neighborhoods deemed unlivable. When that hope is finally extinguished is when the real surge in suicides might occur, Moore said.

"Suicide for most part is not a spontaneous decision," he said. "It's a build-up of hopelessness over time with an underlying theme being loss of control. If an individual feels they have no way to control what is happening to them and can't do anything to change what is making them so miserable, that's when life becomes a deal breaker and they try to think of a way to get out of the emotional pain they're in."

And sometimes, Greve said, it makes no sense at all.

"I had a call from woman in Texas. She had a 10-year old daughter who was doing very well in school. They evacuated from New Orleans in October. A short time later the girl hung herself. Sometimes I think the number of reported suicides might be low."

* * * * * * * * * *

The New York Times ran an editorial on Sunday, the day of the Chris Owens' suicide, proclaiming New Orleans a city on the brink of extinction. This followed on the heels of an editorial by the editor of the Times-Picayune printed in the Washington Post, I believe, or maybe it was the Times, saying much the same thing.

Help us goddammit or kill us.

We run the risk of playing fools to a government of lies.

A valuable role to be sure in a modern tragedy.

Three months after the storm, these are the pleasant days. We are happy to be alive and surrounded by friends who have momentarily proclaimed their allegiance to this fallen city.

But how long can it last?

Thanksgiving is past and Christmas is upon us but it is hard to latch onto that holiday cheer. We lost a good month of living and it has had the effect of putting us all a good month behind the rest of the country.

We're just trying to catch our breath and just when we get a thick intake of oxygen, we raise our heads up from the floods and find ourselves surrounded by ornaments and multi-colored lights and fat, bearded men looking to get it on with 10-year-old mall chicks dressed like Easter hookers desperate for their fix of nine-fisted Hanukah penetration.

My sense of balance has turned on me.

And so it goes.

Mayor Nagin and his Bring Back New Orleans commission is touring the country, holding town hall meetings in places like Baton Rouge and Houston and Atlanta, those places thick with banished New Orleanians, updating them on our progress and listening to their concerns.

And their concerns go a little something like this.......

You left us to die.
We want to come home and
Return to our lives.
But what do we have left except
Flood-mud and upside-down houses?
And 30 miles of corpses and boats on lampposts
And blackouts and our memories that fade like
The faces of our spouses before they dipped under the
Blackened waters with the abandoned dogs and
Wheelchair-bound geriatrics?

The big question is whether the levees will be rebuilt.

No se Paco.

The second is, "When will those neighborhoods most damaged be rebuilt?"

I knew a guy who lived in St. Bernard Parish. A few weeks after it all descended into hell, he returned to his flooded-out home to retrieve what he could. And what he could retrieve, the totality of his salvageable possessions, fit neatly into a Ziplock sandwich bag.

"It will take years upon years to rebuild," he said.

It was an honest answer but not one palatable for a politician. Hope must be provided to those who are in the dark, in Atlanta and Houston and the bulging, ever-expanding diaspora of New Orleans evacuees.

Most people from New Orleans, during the course of their lives, never venture outside of the city. And some, specifically the poor, never cross the borders of their neighborhoods. Outer space is two miles down the road.

But the storm changed all of that.

There are plenty of reports that claim these people, this displaced population, have found a better way of life in their new homes, that they are establishing roots and sucking on rosaries thanking the spirits for this water-logged lottery ticket out of New Orleans.

I think Barbara Bush summed up the glorious fortunes of the evacuated souls of New Orleans best when she said the following about the thousands of families dumped onto the floor of the Houston Astrodome.

"What I'm hearing, which is sort of scary, is they all want to stay in Texas. Everyone is so overwhelmed by the hospitality. And so many of the people in the arena here, you know, were underprivileged anyway, so this is working very well for them."

Oh Barbara! You nasty wench! You hot Cro-Magnon mama! If I never knew you ejected Georgie-boy Junior from betwixt your ham hock nerve-endings I would devote the remainder of my days to the seductive, rhythmic pulsations of your black heart.

The truth, Barbara, is that there is no substitute for New Orleans. No matter the quality of schools in Houston, the abundance of jobs or the absence of execution-bullets spit out by murder-happy babies, the people of New Orleans are the people of New Orleans.

It is a sickness.

It is an addiction.

It is what it is.

And I don't pretend to speak for the masses. For sure there are tens of thousands of former New Orleanians who are pig-shit happy to shed from their spines these strangling coils of the Big Easy. But there are just as many people who have gotten used to that kinky, oxygen-deprived kick we get wandering through the Quarter or the Ninth or Gert Town, flush with pride, knowing that we exist in one of the last original outposts of humanity while the rest of the country is drowning in a sea of mini-malls and Entertainment Tonight broadcasts obsessed with the latest red carpet hits and misses.

And yet, Barbara dear, you slip your hands under your doormat breasts, searching for the warmth that is so tragically missing from these words of mine, confused by my inability to recognize this moment in time, this door that has opened, granting me a once-in-a-lifetime opportunity to better myself, to get the fuck out of Dodge and climb to the top of the 76-rung, stars and stripes ladder that never exceeded 14 rungs in New Orleans.

Where is the warmth?

Where is the gratitude?

"I'm Barbara Bush goddammit! My slaves are free to come and go as they please so long as they are in by 8 p.m. to massage life into my vulva and up by 6 a.m. to finish the job."

Either way.

The point is that my friend from St. Bernard said it is going to take years, if not decades, for his former home to return to form. And since he has a wife and kids to care for, he hit the exit ramp.

And he is gone.

And he is not alone.

Nagin asserts his promise to rebuild everything, but a promise is not a home and the longer these promises go unfulfilled, the odds of a majority of the excommunicated returning lessen by the day, no matter the severity of their New Orleans jones.

And as time passes and the recovery lags, suspicions and conspiracy theories mount, the most common of which is that the city dynamited the Industrial Canal, flooding the Ninth Ward, the poor black community, to save the French Quarter and the wealthy white bastions of Santa Claus sentimentalities.

For the poor blacks who have been shit on their entire lives, what else are they to believe?

Our Pigfucker-in-Chief George Bush scoffs at the idea that race played a part in relief efforts. He said, "The good men and women in the helicopters rescuing people off of rooftops didn't ask whether the people they were rescuing were black or white. All they saw were Americans in trouble."

He said this with a patriotic zeal and self-righteous certainty, scoffing at the critics who attempted to undermine his self-congratulatory Americana noblesse.

How dare these Democratic partisans attack the emergency workers who risked their lives to save the darkies of New Orleans.

How dare they insinuate that the Coast Guard cherry-picked who would be saved and who would die based on race.

But oh Georgie, you dumb, finger-fucking bastard--you still don't get it.

We're not pointing fingers at the men and women in the helicopters, we're pointing the fingers at YOU.

But it was a nice try. And the media hack interviewing you let it slide as they have your entire life.

Fuck it. The keys of my computer are now thick with the blood that has been pouring out of my nose ever since your wretched name entered the equation.

I need a moment to rest, to regroup and temper the pond-skipping beat of my raging heart.

Too late.

We've postponed, indefinitely, our local elections that would have included the mayoral race and the potential beheading of Nagin. They were to take place in February.

Some proclaim if Iraq could hold elections under such dire circumstances why not New Orleans?

I say delay them. There are only 70,000 people occupying New Orleans, the majority white. Why not wait until we can ensure that the evacuees have the best chance of voting?

As for the argument insisting that we are obliged to hold elections simply because the fucking Iraqis have done the same under more extreme circumstances.......well, if we are at the point where we have to follow the lead and live up to the democratic structure and progress of Iraq, then let's just get it over with and dig out our hearts with severed gator tails and dump them in the town square as an offering to our collective stupidity.

The minute we use the Iraqi democratic process as a guideline for our own political activities is the day we......well.......see my previous reference to reptilian self-abuse.

But what do I know?

More than you or I think.

Something like that.

I have flashes of clarity amidst the constant stream of booze and chemicals that rush through my veins.

But now is not the time to cast aspersions on myself.

I'm too busy casting lines out into the female gene pool for a few hours of peace.

A few hours of peace.

Mundane living has turned into the ugly fantastic.

There is no longer any such thing as a quick trip to the supermarket. With only a handful of stores open, and every one operating on limited hours, each trip takes a lifetime of waiting in death-creeping lines.

Our nerves are frayed and sharpened to spike-like specifications. We are all on edge so we jam our bodies into the bars with prayers of salvation.

But the crowds, the goddamn crowds, the fat-bouncing shoulders pounding into us, jamming us with hard hips that give no quarter and swinging elbows that feel no obstruction and offer no apologies. It's getting too much to take and I think soon I'll break.

The people-masses and moving man-piles are omnipresent and ever-maddening. And yet we are forced to make do.

Recently graduated lawyers are forced to tend bar with job prospects obsolete.

The money is good though the future is not.

But we all continue on, not knowing what will be when the calendar kills its own.

Nagin appeared before congress today and pleaded for help, for the 30th fucking time. He said we need levees and housing after which we can point fingers and screw each other to the wall.

The members of Congress thanked him for his time, adjourned to the rec-room underneath the Senate floor, popped in a tape of Hurricane Katrina coverage and took deep swigs off of a gallon bottle of Jim Beam each time a poor black person appeared on the screen, screaming to be saved.

Ten minutes in they were blind drunk.

"Let's call Nagin and tell him we've managed to secure $478.35 in recovery funds," Rep. Jim Sensenbrenner shouted, drooling rusty, brown foam on his Red Lobster bib. "And we'll tell him they don't even have to repay us."

"How about we crank call some Houston shelters," the honorable Sen. Ted Stevens from Alaska offered. "Hello? Mrs. Jackson? We've located the whereabouts of your daughter. Well, not all of your daughter. We got her right arm but have it on good intel that some more of her is in a Chinese restaurant in Dubuque. Wang's Dynasty. That's right. Cheney said she was delicious. Ha, ha, ha, ha. Stupid negroes."

Sixth Entry: Jan. 12 2006.
Santa Sucked a Reindeer....

I'M A GOOD PERSON.

I PROMISE.

IT'S JUST THAT I GOT A TIC IN MY MIND AND A DEMON IN MY BACKYARD.

Time to spread some X-Mas cheer.

Bush pledged another $1.6 billion or so to the construction of our levee system and the House approved $29 billion in aid. It don't mean shit until the money is in hand but there it is, a few steps in the right direction.

Maybe it's the image of Santa crawling down my chimney in white fishnet stockings that has me feeling tender of testicle, but Oh my sweet crimson Christ, that eavesdropping, torture Queen of a president has finally come through for us.

Please forgive me Georgie-boy for fantasizing about your untimely demise. No need to get into specifics as I'm sure you're reading these words as I write them, your left hand down your Thor pajama pants, your right down Cheney's leather-spiked onesey, waiting for me to spill some un-American propaganda.

I must confess that some are accusing you of a sleight-of-hand maneuver, trying to pass off already promised cash as brand new funding, but I'm gonna give you the benefit of the doubt.

Just this one time. I'm sure you won't let me down. I may be a battered son of the sewage, constantly allowing you to grind my head in the shit out of some false hope that one day you'll get it, the way the world is supposed to work, kindness and brotherly love and all that crap. And every time you seem to let myself and the greater part of that non-crucifix-humping segment of humanity down. All laughing and rubbing ointments on your joints for better flexibility the next go-round.

But I got a feeling this time you may surprise me (as I slug down the last of this handle of gin and throw down the remaining pills in my piggy bank).

Right?

Hell, I don't know. All I do know is that the suicide rate in New Orleans is skyrocketing and I believe we are on the brink of some serious racial tension.

Sixteen cops, 15 white, one black, surrounded a brain-addled 38-year-old black man wielding a knife on St. Charles Avenue. According to news reports he tried to smack a clerk at the nearby Walgreen's after his credit card was denied. How that confrontation resulted in a bullet-riddled corpse lying in the middle of St. Charles Avenue is anyone's guess. Our esteemed new chief of police, Warren Riley, said the shooting was justified. Nine shells were found on the scene.

They say the man lunged at a cop who was between 8 and 16 feet away. And that was that.

Boom, boom, boom let's go back to my room so we can do it all night and kill some……..

Strange thing is that there seems to be less talk about this recent incident than when the NOPD beat the blood out of the retired teacher on Bourbon Street two months ago. But the combined impact of these events has created a ripple effect that threatens the strange peace that has settled over the dried mud of our city.

Two nights ago at the Avenue a large group of black kids got into it with the ex-marine bartender and several of his friends.

The Avenue is not a white bar; it is a local haunt, not a dive but close enough. It is a place people go to rip open the seams of their livers. It is a bar for alcoholics and fiends and people who just don't give a fuck.

Come one come all.

But a strange thing happened after the storm. On the walls of the men's bathroom someone scrawled racist propaganda, all forms of vile, anti-black rhetoric. Grossly distorted pictures of black men drowning in the Ninth Ward. It took more than a month before management got around to painting over the rotten images but the sentiment of these anonymous scrawlers made itself known to everyone who entered that dank piss-closet.

Racism has always been a part of New Orleans. Some say to get to the South you have to drive outside of the city, and to a point that's true. All manner of monstrous activity and unholy behavior is, if not condoned, overlooked. But to say New Orleans is separate from the South is naïve.

It's true that segregation to a large extent does not exist in New Orleans. Beyond the wedding cake mansions lining St. Charles Avenue, those stately homes well-positioned for the street car-riding tourists to "ooh" and "ahh" at, just two blocks in either direction, you can find low-income and minority families trying to make a go of it.

This is the glory of New Orleans, the core of its spirit. Unlike other major cities where the poor and black have been systematically pushed to the far edges, far from the bright, white eyes of the moneymakers and cash-raining tourists, in New Orleans it's one block white one block black. And I like to believe that this haphazard and random population scheme has engendered a feeling of community between the races. In most cities, the only places where whites and blacks mix are in Walgreen's or on buses.

Not in New Orleans.

In New Orleans every facet of life is touched by its black heritage.

In New Orleans the two races second-line together and drink together and bounce to jazz beats together.

In New Orleans we smile and call each other "baby" and embrace each other as neighbors.

It's the closeness of our homes that gives us this rare closeness as people.

That's the idealistic version. That's the vision of New Orleans we celebrate and rightfully so.

But there's another New Orleans.

And this other New Orleans is just like any other city, any other town—north, south, east, west—where the worst in mankind just can't help itself.

And in post-Katrina New Orleans, it feels like this other New Orleans is at war with its idealistic sister, and as time goes by the bruises and scars are mounting.

And I suppose this war was in full rage before the storm. I never blinded myself to this reality. But after, it seems like we have more to lose, that the hate is all the more disgusting, more threatening to our fragile world.

As a white drunk it is not uncommon for some similarly white drunk to take a seat next to me at a bar and strike up a conversation. And it will be the same shit you hear every day at any given bar. But sometimes, maybe one out of every 10 times, in the middle of the conversation, my new friend will suddenly ask something like, "You know what's wrong with this city?"

"What?"

And he'll say, all calm-like, "It's all these fucking niggers."

Such pearls of wisdom are uttered with a frightening familiarity, as if, because I too am white, of course I'll share their demented racial viewpoint.

And when those words come out of their mouth it feels like evil vomited.

Wink, wink.

Jigaboo.

Spearchucker.

It's OK man. We're all God's chosen children.

Got to stick together.

Circle the white wagons.

And it works both ways.

There are those among the black community who savor that savory hatred of the white man, the fucking pink pricks who deserve nothing more than spit and spite.

And among both of these ignorant groups, there is a powerful sense of justification for their respective venom.

This has always been a part of New Orleans, but the dynamic has changed and will continue to devolve into something new. The emotional wreckage and spiritual torture of the storm has left our hearts empty, desirous of an enemy we can anoint as the anti-Christ. And for some, for too many, he has been discovered in the gene pool of the opposing race.

I could be wrong, but I've seen and heard the evidence.

It's no secret that many blacks believe the levees were dynamited to wipe out their neighborhoods in order to save the French Quarter where the whites run rampant.

It is no secret that many whites credit the drop in violence after Katrina to the exodus of the black population.

The hurricane confirmed the dark suspicions of both groups, that the other group was the source of their misery.

Proof.

Finally.

Justification.

At last.

This is the new wrinkle of this new New Orleans that is beginning to rear its deformed head.

Many in the city, those who stayed through the aftermath and chaos, remain on war footing. There is now a take-no-more-shit attitude that has taken root.

No more goddammit.

We will no longer suffer the fools.

The blacks.

The whites.

And in the mix is a trigger-happy police force.

They say they are trained only to use deadly force when threatened.

They say they were not trained to aim for the leg of a knife-wielding suspect, like that crazed 38-year-old in the middle of St. Charles Avenue. According to our esteemed police chief Warren Riley, even if the officers shot the man in his thigh, he could have continued to pose a threat, a wobbling, stumbling threat in the face of a battalion of armed officers. They said they maced him but it had no effect.

Stun guns were not an option. Only the SWAT team is in possession of those electrical firecrackers and they were not on the scene.

Stun guns are too dangerous, the NOPD brass says. There have been over 70 documented cases of stun gun-related deaths last year alone. Better to blast the fucker in the chest with the real thing and let the water sort'em out.

Yeah, that idealized vision of New Orleans seems to be drifting further into the realm of unicorns and soul-mates.

Soon the city will set up trailer sites that will allow many displaced individuals to return to New Orleans. Just about every council member is desperately fighting to prevent the placement of these temporary mobile cities in their own communities. And they are backed by their constituents who are holding fast to the infamous NIMBY philosophy--Not in My Backyard.

They use as an excuse the lowering of property values and the seizure of prized parks and green spaces to fight the trailer parks. But the true fear is that these trailers will house former residents of the projects, i.e. the blacks, who will bring crime, drugs and violence. Given the state of the city and the misery that many displaced families suffered, the selfishness of NIMBY is reprehensible.

As I said, New Orleans has always been an integrated city--one block wealthy and white, the next poor and black. This often resulted in confrontation, but it also provided people the opportunity to mix and mingle and break down walls traditionally built in more gentrified cities.

But now that these communities have been violently separated--one forced out of town, the other firmly entrenched on high ground--a struggle has arisen for possession of our broken home.

This is not a struggle that will be assumed by the majority, but it is never the majority that makes the most noise in such circumstances. It is the people who scrawl vicious and racist sentiments on bathroom walls and those who level charges of racism on anything white and breathing.

These small subcultures will force the rest of us to come to terms with something that has been festering under our feet for decades.

I'm not saying there will be a race war, but small, isolated violent confrontations between whites and blacks will increase.

Of course, this is all conjecture coming from a brain-addled drunk who already has a knife picked out for when he inevitably will find himself in the middle of St. Charles Avenue babbling like a loon, demanding a shot of Patron and a line of blow or else the "pigs are gonna get it."

My friends and family will watch the nightly news in horror as the horseshoe of cops surround me.

I'll be blabbering and flabbering, jabbering like an idiot because I can't get my grabby hands on some gabby goo.

"What did he say?" the cops will ask.

"I have no idea. It sounded Arabic."

"Oh God! He's got a forked tongue! He's speaking in multiple-syllables! Aim for the heart!"

No, I'll mumble. I'm sorta right in the head. I'm sorta sane. I promise. It's just that I'll stabby the crabby blue cops and cabbies and from top to bottom and the listless dreams that inevitably fight me.

Oh god. That didn't come out right.

I sound insane.

"He's fucking crazy and that knife of his has got blood on it! Move in boys!"

This isn't going well. Why can't I verbalize these sane thoughts of mine that sound so reasonable in the core of my brain? How in the fuck do I find myself surrounded by the armed boys in blue in the middle of St. Charles Avenue with a knife in hand, unable to form a single coherent sentence?

I'm a good person. I promise. It's just that I got a tic in my mind and a demon in my backyard.

Goddammit! All I want is some of the white shiny and a shot of the gold briny that used to get me through moments like these. So please have some mercy and fucking shoot me!

"You heard him boys!"

No! That wasn't me! I didn't mean to say that! I don't want to die!

Goddammit! I can't communicate like I want to! If you could only get inside my mind and understand my sanity and the source of my profanity. I'm not a lunatic. This isn't me. I'm trying to get through to you, but I got this knife and I got a lust for the slashy-slashy, the bloody blade cuttin' down the dirty dirty.

Shit.

That was the nail in the coffin.

Ok.

I give up.

It's no use.

This is my fault.

It's ok guys.

I don't blame you.

You're just doing your job.

And from your perspective, I'm a mad-righteous heretic.

It's no use trying to explain myself anymore since every reasonable sentiment formed in my head comes spewing out of my mouth like the prayers of a pit viper.

So let me make it easy on you.

What I want to say is this, "My heart aches the same as yours."

But when I speak it comes out something like this, "I'm a gin-drinkin', knife-stabbin', ready-made corpse! So come get me!"

"You heard the nutty bastard boys. Shoot the fucker."

I spent the day after the New Year driving my newly resurrected '88 Ford Bronco II through the lower Ninth Ward. After crossing the Industrial Canal I took the first left and drove slowly along the shores of Armageddon.

This was my first viewing of the lower Ninth, or the Mighty Nine as it was once known to its residents. By this point, everyone knows about the Ninth Ward--a poor black community chock-a-block with gangstas and dealers and midnight slayings. But that would be an incomplete picture of a neighborhood that was also the proud home of generations of homeowners.

Sure, there were large areas that would fit that nightmare description. But there were also oak-lined streets and playgrounds and neatly manicured lawns and well-kept homes where friends and family would gather to laugh and barbecue to that indelible New Orleans brass soundtrack.

I ain't saying it wasn't a dangerous place. But to many it was much more.

Now, it's a wasteland.

Most of the houses left standing are brick. Everything else was either swept away, leaving nothing but the foundation and front stoop, or levitated and thrown into the middle of the street, blasted by gravity into a pile of debris.

The break in the levee was visible as was the barge that crashed through it, a giant hulk of steel dumped onto a single row of houses. It was a Sunday when I drove to the Ninth. The streets teemed with slow-moving cars of gawkers and onlookers, curious to experience firsthand what we've all seen ad-nauseam on the news.

And then there were the former residents of the Mighty Nine who moved like lost specters through the rubble. They were instantly recognizable, not only because they were black but because of how they surveyed the scene, gently shaking their heads, eyes carefully moving over old memories, cautious in their inspection so as not to miss a familiar object that might trigger a precious image of better days.

"The sad thing is," an older man said, "is that no one will know how great it really was."

As I made my way down the road, a woman smiled and asked, "Are you from here?"

"I live in New Orleans, but not here," I said. "Did you live here?"

"Yes," she said with a motherly smile.

"What are you going to do?"

"I'm living in Pineville now," she said. "I know I'm never moving back to New Orleans." She lived on the other side of the road. She lost everything. I wished her good luck and moved on.

"It's like going to a funeral," a woman behind me said, "except you don't know who died."

I spent about two hours in the Ninth Ward. The plan was to continue on to St. Bernard and then on to eastern New Orleans but I had enough death and destruction for one day. As I made my way out I stopped to talk to a young attorney with the National Lawyers Guild, a group working to ensure the residents of the Ninth Ward are not screwed out of their homes by bulldoze-happy politicians.

She asked how long I had been in the Ninth Ward and I told her two hours. She said next time I come to wear a face mask because of all the toxins in the air. "If you don't wear a mask you'll feel it later," she said.

And sure enough, later in the day my head was splitting, though that could have been from any number of substances recently ingested. Why blame it on the air?

On my way to work the other day I passed an overturned SUV on the side of the road, its black paint awash in the blue and red lights of a squad car. Across the street from my office building, in the parking lot of a Winn-Dixie supermarket, there was an old Buick engulfed in flames, fat streams of black smoke spiraling out of the mass of angry orange heat. The owners, an elderly couple, stood several hundred feet away amidst the crowd of onlookers who snapped shots with cell phones. The couple held hands. They looked nervous and scared, old and alone. What this meant to their lives, I don't know. All I had to go on was that look on their faces, the childlike fear often found in the recently ravaged and those screaming towards an unexpected end. In other words, damn near everyone in New Orleans.

These two vehicular massacres had nothing to do with the hurricane. It's just another surreal day in New Orleans where nothing makes sense--that persistent state of random madness that has become the norm.

On New Year's Eve, an out-of-state construction worker stood on the levee at the end of Carrollton Avenue with a local he befriended. The man was a Vietnam Vet. He traveled hundreds of miles to help the city rebuild and make some cash in the process. The two friends stood on the levee and watched the fireworks through a thick fog that rolled low over the city. As the pair looked to the sky, after a series of nearby firecracker blasts, the man said, "I've been shot."

And he dropped to his knees.

The woman ran into Cooter Brown's, a nearby bar. "My friend's been shot!" she screamed. "My friend's been shot!"

For as long as anyone can remember, shooting guns into the air at midnight on New Year's Eve in New Orleans has been a tradition. People are warned to seek cover, go inside come midnight, but no one has been hurt since 1994 when a man was last slain by a falling bullet.

Now, on the first New Year's Eve since Katrina, some gun-happy shithead fired off a few rounds, one of which sunk into this man's back and made its way into his spine.

A cook from Cooter Brown's held the man as he lay on the levee.

The cook thought the guy was dying.

He wasn't.

He wasn't that lucky.

The Vietnam Vet, this big-hearted visitor who found himself entranced by our boggy depot at the mouth of the Mississippi, he was very much alive. Half of him at least. The rest of him, the walking part, was paralyzed.

And what was left to say?

Thanks for the help kind sir. Thanks for coming down to good ol' New Orleans and helping us rebuild. Now grab your fucking wheelchair and get the fuck outta Dodge. We have enough emotional cripples rolling their shattered hearts through our blood-soaked streets. We have our share of knife-wielding mental patients and sadist cops and fire-popping Buicks and bathroom-scrawling racists. If you don't mind, we don't have time to tend to your needs, so push your circular legs onto one of the five weekly flights carrying the broken and horrified out of New Orleans to better shores and be done with it. We wish you well.

I'm not exactly sure what to say.

We're broken-hearted as a rule.

And as hard as it is for me to say, we may not have enough left in our broken hearts to tend to yours.

So I wish you safe passage to wherever you came, far away from this godforsaken place, this city that so many of us have made a blood oath to preserve and protect no matter what, no matter the collateral damage.

Such as yourself.

These are the dark times.

It don't get any better, right?

That's not true.

It was better.

Four months ago.

It was better.

For all of us.

Seventh Entry
January 12, 2006, - February 20, 2006,

---- If a Black TREE Fell in theFoREst

SOMEWHERE SOMETHING IS BURNING, SMOLDERING,

BEING ERASED FROM OUR REALITY,

CREATING ANOTHER
HOLE
THAT WON'T BE FILLED FOR YEARS.

According to the Times-Picayune of the 3,200 people still listed as missing five months after Hurricane Katrina, 400 are from badly flooded areas such as eastern New Orleans and St. Bernard Parish. Officials are asking for another body sweep.

Now here's the part that hit me: "It's possible some of the missing were washed into Lake Pontchartrain or that their bodies remain in the rubble that blankets much of the city. Over the past several weeks some families returning to wrecked homes have found remains of relatives inside."

That's some chilling ass shit.

And that last sentence of mine was some truly impressive, high-minded writing.

I am a literary giant with a bag filled with about seven offensive words I sprinkle throughout this historic public record.

Temper your awe and read on.

You may think I would be tempted to weigh in on Nagin's thunderous Chocolate City remark—"I don't care what people are saying Uptown or wherever they are. This city will be chocolate at the end of the day." I'm not. The entrails at Fox News seem to have that infinitely important topic well-covered. So I'll leave it to their cyclopic hand-jobbing pundits to beat that subject into the ground and through the spongy heads of their pumpkin-fucking viewers.

Does any of that make sense?

Of course not. I'm an Oompa Loompa hooked on the dark mistress known as the coca. Or is it the cocoa?

Either way, it's time to move on.

A quick side note: When I first returned I wondered whether there would be a long period marked by an absence of drugs. What became of the dealers? Well, either they stayed in New Orleans through the storm, dedicated to their mystical craft or, after safely evacuating, they regrouped, gathered en mass in Atlanta, and returned as soon as hell would permit, for the drugs are once again freely flowing through the bars and taverns and alleys.

I won't divulge how I know these things but trust me......urrrrrr …..ummmm…….what?

The barking of the dogs and the weather vane in my brain....
Oh my sweet Chocolate City, how I love thee milky white thighs and fish are frightening.
Don't mind these words of mine. I am but a simple victim of my surroundings--surging Godiva riptides and godless, caramel-filled harlots.
Goddammit. This was supposed to be my state of the city speech but things seemed to have turned inside out. I'm as high as a motherfucker.

Time to regroup.

There's a little shithead Jefferson Parish Councilman named Chris Roberts. He was just 21 years old when he was elected to the school board in 1998. So now he's 28 going on 29.
This foul little fuck was supposedly amassing a respectable record. And then Katrina hit.
Maybe you've heard the story about the Crescent City Connection, the bridge connecting New Orleans with the West Bank. After the storm, several hundred people, mostly black, in a desperate attempt to escape the water-logged Thunderdome known as New Orleans, began walking across the Crescent City Connection. Halfway across they were met by the Gretna police who not only told them to turn the fuck around but to emphasize their point, they fired a couple shotgun rounds into the air.
Gretna officials said they didn't have any food, water or shelter to care for the huddled masses. So they sent them back to hell, from whence they came. And where, apparently, Gretna officials felt these poor souls belonged.
One of my friends was part of the starving brigade that tried to cross the bridge. She said the cops warned the crowd that the West Bank wasn't going to become another New Orleans. And then they let loose with their shotgun invocations.
So where does little Chris Roberts enter the picture?
As a councilman of Jefferson Parish, Roberts passed a resolution that said Jefferson would spend as much money as needed to defend the Gretna police against legal action. Roberts apparently had little sympathy for the plight of the evacuees.
Here is his immortal quote:
"Had the individuals adhered to the mandatory evacuation order they would not be in the situation they were in."
Oh silly little sissy Chrissy wants the brutes from New Orleans to know that he is in charge, that he is willing to march on their homes with burning crosses of public cash.

Ring around the noosey,
A pocket full of goosey-steps
Blackies, blackies
They all fall down.

But Chrissy ain't alone.
The other day I picked up a guy from the decimated St. Bernard Parish hitching on Magazine Street outside of Le Bon Temps Roule. It wasn't my intention to pick him up but he ran in front of my truck, arms waving like a scarecrow, mouth screwed in a grimace.
"Hey! Hey! Hey!"
"What?"
"Are you headed downtown? Can you give me a ride?"
I paused, looked the guy up and down and estimated my odds of survival should he unsheathe a knife or make a go for my neck with his xylophone teeth.
"Ok," I said. "Get in. But I'm not going far."
So he hopped in, gave thanks, and we were on our way.
The conversation began like most do nowadays in New Orleans--How'd you make out during the storm? Is your house standing?
Spilled tales of survival.
Glad to be alive but life now is nothing but misery. He said he lost everything and was now living with his parents. He said he was considering a move out of town, maybe to Savannah.
"Why Savannah?" I asked.
Brace for it.
"I heard it's like New Orleans, a small town," he said. "But without all the niggers and spics."
Bingo baby.
Now we're at the heart of it.
Niggers and spics.
"How about Austin," I offered.
"Fuck no man. More spics than there are here taking all of our jobs."
I pulled over and said, "This is where I'm stopping. I'm gonna have to let you off here."
He crawled out without protest.
"Hey man, you think you can loan me $5? I spent all I had on a beer at Le Bon Temps. "
"No comprende," I said.
"Come on man," he shouted as I pulled back into the street. "I lost everything! All I need is a few bucks!"

I've talked about the ever-present racism of New Orleans, the bigoted confidences shared by good ol' boys who assume, just because you're white, that you too are a craven example of inhumanity. A week ago the point hit home.

Suds, an elfin drunk I enjoy rapping with at the Avenue, got banned for life for calling the porter a "crow."

Quick back-story.

In the last section I talked about the racist scrawlings and bigoted graffiti that appeared on the bathroom walls of the Avenue shortly after I returned from my Katrina banishment. Awful, Sambo, spearchucking drawings depicting the inner workings of the worst kind of racists, celebrating the drowning of black men in the lower Ninth. One of the crude renderings was of the porter, a wiry, middle-aged black man with a beard like a billy goat.

I've known Suds for years--a kind, quiet guy, the type you enjoy talking to for hours, who listens and usually has something interesting to give so far as conversation.

I always made a point to go out of my way to sit with him, his little elfin legs dangling several feet above the ground, the bells on his pointed shoes jingling and jangling as he beeped away in his dog-whistle voice about making cookies and licorice whips.

Suds was about 40 or so, four-feet-five-inches tall, always with a smile. Never known to have a girlfriend though he talked about some lost loves. I always figured he was gay.

"Sure Suds, Tony sounds like a real nice gal. Too bad that didn't work out."

Stupid little elf.

Anyway, one day the bartender from the Avenue called me.

"Rich, you'll never believe what happened? Kyle 86ed Suds and Peek-a-Boo Paul."

Peek-a-Boo Paul was a sour spectacle of a human being and a mean little racist elf who also happened to be a good friend of Suds. He was an Avenue regular, a fixture. He sat on his stool, most of the time by himself, sucking down the Avenue special, a 36-ounce mug of beer. And about halfway down his sixth, Peek-a-Boo Paul would throw his green pointed hat on the ground, jump on top of his stool and hop up and down, squealing mumbled devil-talk about hues and pigments and hard to reach candy canes.

I hated Peek-a-Boo Paul. Whenever he spilled his down-syndrome racism on me, I got into it with him and it got ugly and the more shots of tequila we did the uglier it got.

"You're a dumb motherfucker," I said.

"Watch your fucking mouth Rich," Peek-a-Boo Paul said. "I've killed people in my life."

"With what? One of those metal arms with the pincers at the end that old people use to reach jars of pickles on the top shelves of their cabinets? You fucking Lilliputian."

But after awhile I got to feeling sorry for the guy. We would talk about his construction job and the many times his boss fired him because of his rage problem. At times he even showed sympathy for the Hispanic laborers when they were screwed over by the contractors.

Even the devil sometimes feeds a stray cat.

Stupid little Peek-a-Boo Paul with his beer stein half his height and his shaved pea-head and his brain retardation that kept him at arms length from breasts and the long legs and milky white sides of the normal-sized women he would never know by touch, only through dreams and the cracks in his neighbors' curtains.

So Peek-a-Boo Paul and Suds were good friends. Always thought it a bit strange. Sure, elves typically travel in pairs to protect themselves against hawk attacks but why would Suds befriend a racist fuck like Peek-a-Boo Paul? But there they were, the freak-show forefathers of a crossbred nation.

"Why the hell did Suds get 86ed?" I asked the Avenue bartender.

"He called Billy the porter a crow. And Billy went wild."

"A crow? What the hell does that mean? I've heard every racial epithet but I've never heard crow. That must be some deep dark southern racist shit."

"It gets worse," she said. "I heard Suds tell Paul when he was going to the bathroom that he was going to the 'mural room.'"

"The mural room? Are you saying that Suds was one of the guys who wrote that sick shit on the walls?"

"Apparently so. Suds is as big a racist as Paul."

A few days earlier Suds was telling me a story and he led it off by saying, "I was talking to two of my racist friends....." Now I thought he called them his racist friends to distinguish himself from them, like saying, "I was talking to two of my black friends." But it was more like, "I was talking to two of my skydiving buddies."

Suds and Peek-a-Boo Paul were both skydivers.

I thought of all the times I sat with Suds, truly enjoying his presence. I thought he was a good guy and looked forward to our hour-long talks. He never gave himself away, never hinted at his darker persona, never bragged about his affinity for white-power graffiti. The mural wall, spoken about with reverence, as if it were some hallowed accomplishment they labored over with precision and surgical-Klan love.

Crow? I had no idea what it meant. I pictured Suds saying it with that smile of his, that toothy grin that looked harmless but was, in reality, backed by a cloaked evil he shared with only his most favored racist buddies.

And this realization, this de-hooding of Suds enraged me. And the rage consumed me. We have so few things to hold onto in these post-storm days. The only things that matter are the bonds we share with our friends; the only people who can relate to these mounting layers of insanity that increasingly separate us from all of them, the people on the outside. And Suds, you simple-minded midget, you fucking robbed me of a comfortable corner I could once claim as a refuge, you along with your psychotic, white supremacist cabbage patch friend who you stole away with into the bathroom where the two of you egg-shaped muppets giggled in unison as you gripped log-sized black markers with your stubby fingers and scrawled coded symbols for, "We are the lollipop-sucking guild."

You betrayed this, our union of survivors.

But the thing that bothers me the most, Suds, is that I will be forced to look back at this moment, and your placid liquid smile, as the breaking point when I understood that there is, and never was, a union of survivors. That in the aftermath of catastrophe, people such as yourself, will milk back to life the deformed offspring of hate with your pixie stix teats.

You dumb fucking midgets.

There.

That's a piece of my own hatred to keep you warm at night when your Klan underoos and entwined sausage limbs aren't up to the task.

We're starting from scratch in New Orleans. A new society with grand hopes and dreams overshadowed by the blitzkrieg that gave us this opportunity to make things better. Three tornadoes touched down in Jefferson Parish a few days ago and wiped out large swaths of homes. One landed a few yards from my office building. It hopped down Veterans and made its way into the Lakeview neighborhood that had been decimated by Katrina. Homeowners had spent weeks, for some months, repairing flood-damaged properties only to see a goddamn weather anomaly devastate all of their hard work. Gutted homes now nothing more than slabs.

Three days ago a fire broke out at the Coliseum Theater, a New Orleans landmark. On my way home from work I saw helicopters carrying massive buckets of water over the burning structure, dumping 2,000 gallons of Mississippi River down on the inferno. The next morning a fire broke out in the Bywater, wiping out three homes and damaging two others.

I sit still for hours afraid the friction of my tattered rags will start a new blaze.

Two weeks ago on a Sunday I drove into the Treme, the oldest black neighborhood in the country, to take part in the largest second line since Katrina. It kicked off outside of St. Augustine Church and was meant to be a signal to the city and the world that the black community was coming back, that their spirit lives on.

But the Treme is one of those neighborhoods on the critical list, and its heart, St. Augustine Church, has been threatened with the stake.

Church closure could cripple Treme

By Richard A. Webster New Orleans CityBusiness Staff Writer

November, 7 2005 -- The 163-year-old St. Augustine Church in Treme survived Hurricane Katrina as it survived hurricanes Betsy and Camille. Yet it may not survive a wave of church closures planned by the Archdiocese of New Orleans.

The Rev. Jerome G. LeDoux, St. Augustine's pastor, said the church suffered minimal damage but repairs could cost $400,000. St. Augustine Church is now targeted for closure by the archdiocese.

"We have insurance through the archdiocese but much of the archdiocese is blasted and they're talking about reopening only 50 percent of the churches," LeDoux said. "I wouldn't look in their direction now for help so we're counting on donations. We need to prove the church can stand on its own."

The archdiocese did not return repeated calls for comment.

Victor Davis, a nine-year resident of Treme who is making a documentary about the neighborhood, said the idea of Treme without St. Augustine is unthinkable.

"People come from all over to speak with Father LeDoux," said Davis. "He is a very important figure in New Orleans and I would think people will be outraged to say the least that anyone would even bring up the notion of closing this church."

Treme is the oldest African-American neighborhood in the United States, home to Congo Square where jazz was born. Since the 1960s, when large swaths of Treme were destroyed to make way for Interstate 10 and Armstrong Park, the community has struggled with violence and poverty, said Norman Smith, director of the Treme Community Education Program.

According to the U.S. Census Bureau report in 2000, the average income in Treme was $19,564 compared with $43,176 for the entire city of New Orleans.

To lose St. Augustine Church, a long-standing symbol of Treme's pride, would signal that one of the most historic areas in New Orleans is being permanently swept away, said Davis.

With St. Augustine targeted for closure, Davis said he worries it will be forgotten in the shadow of other historical landmarks.

"When the statue of Jesus at the back of the St. Louis Cathedral lost a finger during the storm they were all over it, using up all of these resources to find that finger," said Davis. "That's fine and I understand but eight blocks away there's a church with a wall falling off and it's treated like a stepchild. There's no parity."

Unlike Magazine Street and the Central Business District, city-organized teams of volunteer cleanup crews have yet to materialize in sparsely populated Treme. Flies swarm long lines of bloated black garbage bags. Parts of what used to be walls and ceilings spill out into streets pockmarked by deep craters.

On St. Ann Street, a child's red and yellow toy lawnmower sits on the street-level roof of a flattened house.

Across the road, Stanley "Pop" DeDeaux pulls a warm can of Natural Light beer from an un-refrigerated case.

"I ain't no alcoholic," DeDeaux said. "But I ain't running out."

The 67-year-old Vietnam veteran stayed in Treme during Hurricane Katrina in his second-story apartment. For almost two months he has been the only person occupying the Basin Street side of the neighborhood.

DeDeaux's two-story property is one of several in Treme left without power but he said it doesn't bother him.

"I've gotten as old as I am by having patience and not raising my blood pressure and having no stroke or nothing. I'll wait my turn," DeDeaux said.

LeDoux stayed in Treme for eight days after the hurricane so he could watch over St. Augustine and his neighbors, many of whom lacked the means to leave, he said. "It was very spooky before I left because no one had any lights," LeDoux said. "You'd step outside and look up and see what no one in New Orleans sees to any extent — stars and planets all over the sky — a very strange sight."

When LeDoux returned from Baton Rouge Oct. 4 the rectory had power and life slowly crept back into Treme. "We're still waiting for the stores to open but we can walk a couple blocks to the French Quarter," LeDoux said. "Now it's time to dig in and make something new of Treme and New Orleans."

Though Davis said he admires LeDoux's optimism, he worries that the future of Treme and other African-American communities are in doubt because of its high percentage of renters.

According to the 2000 census, renters occupied 2,681, or 78.2 percent, of 3,429 houses in Treme. The percentage of rentals for the rest of New Orleans was 53.5 percent.

"I have owned a house there for three years and I've seen less and less black people and more and more white people," Davis said. "The situation is untenable. I would not be surprised if not just Treme but other traditionally black neighborhoods become 70 percent white."

* * * * * * * * * *

But on this day, on the day of the second line, the heart of the Treme was strong and black.

And goddamn, when I saw Kermit Ruffins leading the charge, horns a blazin', throngs of people dancing down the street, people on porches along the parade route jumping over railings with beers in hands to join the chaos, it felt like that Rebirth soundtrack, that unmistakable sound of New Orleans life.

It was all going to be ok.

We romped through the Treme and down Rampart, the human snake growing in size with each block, picking up and devouring all bystanders who could not resist the pull of the brass bands and the stomp of feet, heads down, arms in the air, spinning on heels.

That goddamn sun was shining on us all.

After all of the shit, we were back to what drew us to New Orleans in the first place, that impulsive desire to bend the brain to the sounds of the sax and the boom, boom, boom of the Tuba.

Heads held high. Beers down the throat.

Block those streets off because we're marching motherfuckers. Everything comes to a stop.

All of our misery and pain.

Everything.

This is the second line, but not just any second line. This is the second line to end all second lines. A declaration of strength. Can you hear us world? Can you see this, what we're capable of, this glorious, rubber-room resistance to last rites?

When the second line turned down Esplanade towards Broad I separated myself from the throngs and headed back to my car.

Everything's going to be ok.

It's still here. The spirit. The celebration. That love of life that has always tied all of New Orleans into one mad, unexplainable knot.

Seven hours later I switched on the evening news.

"Second line ends in tragedy. Gun shots ring out wounding three people."

A young black woman lay in the middle of the street in a puddle of blood.

"I came here from Atlanta where I evacuated to after the storm," a black woman said into the camera. "I came back because this is my home and I wanted to show my support. But this is it for me. Nothing has changed. I don't want to come back to this, the murder and death and foolishness. I'm not coming back again. I'm done with New Orleans."

We can deal with the tornadoes and random fires. But after all the shit we've been through, these senseless random murders committed by single-testicle, latent-homosexual gangbangers are just too goddamn much to take.

Good people who lost everything drove hundreds of miles to the Treme to reunite with friends and family and take part in a second line meant to lift spirits. But the same crippled souls that raped and murdered and looted during the storm, and for decades before that, drove the angels of New Orleans into the depths with quick-fire blasts into the flesh of three innocents.

Before the storm, the murder rate was climbing to record levels. We were experiencing one of the bloodiest of years in New Orleans. After the storm, all of that disappeared. Those terrible days faded as we dealt with the absolute destruction brought on by the failure of the levees.

And now this.
And now the bullets.
And the streets sweated blood.

More than 200,000 homes destroyed and all these fucking punks can think of are turf wars and slights to their non-existent manhood.
The Krewe of Eunuchs is alive and well.
Wash away the blood, clean the wounds and prepare for the next second line.
There's nothing we can do but prepare for our first post-K Mardi Gras and hope for the best.
Unfortunately, we fear the second line was but a precursor and that Carnival will draw the worst of the worst, the opportunity for a citywide bloodletting, a target-rich environment.
And we will all surely suffer as the eyes of the world fall on New Orleans once again.
And in dirty hotel rooms and Labrea tar pits the gunny kids are plotting and rioting over barren lands ripe for graveyard developments.
Mothers and fathers, future ghosts, lift tired smiles for the benefit of their children, telling them everything will be ok. But in a week's time, when the Krewe of Automatic Fire rolls, when the .45 caliber throws perforate parental hearts, these precious dolls will lose the ability to experience anything but vengeance.
And the reflected images of carousels in crystal-innocent eyes will be washed away in a cloud a blood.

The other day, as I was driving to work, the smoky remnants of a distant fire crept over the horizon.
Déjà-vu.
Another reminder that we are living in some apocalyptic nightmare.
Another fire.
More destruction.

Somewhere, something is burning, smoldering, being erased from our reality, creating another hole that won't be filled for years.

But that's just the way it is.

Our city and our lives are peppered with craters, spaces begging to be filled by something, anything.

Relationships are falling apart, family and friends dying, a wave of discontent widening over a dead plain of brown grass and sun-starved children, the pale spawn of whatever it is that happened to us all.

Ahh, but to hell with all of that. Mardi Gras will soon be upon us. And our appetites for booze have grown at a terrifying pace. We live on speed-highs and downer-lows punctuated by momentary bursts of bottle-joy. An outside observer would say we are living on borrowed time, keeping at arms length the ultimate and terrifying breakdowns destined for us all. And with every shot of tequila we push ourselves deeper into denial.

But what would you do?

We are doing what it takes to maintain the illusion of sanity, though some have already made the break, through the wall, into a loving embrace with something psychotic that feels strangely familiar.

Hard to say which scenario will play out for the best.

But with each week comes another body-blow like our crippled president handing us a mere six lines in his State of the Union, a cursory mention of the total destruction of an American city, a historic and one-of-a-kind event.

And we raged and whined and spit on the street and cursed that Texan motherfucker for his indifference to us compared to his bleeding heart compassion for the Iraqis.

But we know better.

He tells the nation that all is going well in New Orleans just as he proclaims all is going well in Iraq. I am uniquely situated to tell you that he is lying about New Orleans which leads me to believe, as I always have, that he is lying about Iraq.

I am on the ground, a witness to the spin and lies.

New Orleans is slowly dying.
You poor fucking Iraqis.

The DruNk Side of FINE...

WE SUCKED ON

BABY BOTTLES

FILLED WITH LSD

AND SNORTED RAILS

OF BLOW OFF OF BABY BONNETS
WORN BY BABY DOLLS PACKED
WITH UPPERS AND DOWNERS.

WE DO BELIEVE IN SELF-GRATIFICATION.
WE DO BELIEVE IN PARISIAN EXCESS......

Note: The first weekend of Mardi Gras passed with little fanfare or insanity. The weather was shit, cold and rainy. Sparse crowds spotted St. Charles Avenue on Saturday for five scheduled parades that flew by in less than two hours.

It didn't feel right, didn't feel like Mardi Gras.

Jesus, this was the one thing we were all looking forward to, that great Carnival to take our minds off of our expanding plain of inner lunacy and outward madness.

National and international papers led with the predictable stories--how can the insensitive, remaining citizens of New Orleans party when people remain homeless, displaced, lost, lonely, desperate, etc.

Or dead.

Lovell Beaulieu, an editor in northwest Indiana, penned an editorial for the Times-Picayune detailing the nature of our sin for insisting on reconvening Mardi Gras.

It sent me into a catatonic rage.

Mr. Beaulieu-

I'm not sure where to start tearing apart your dim-witted and ignorant rant that somehow made it past the editors at the Times-Picayune.

Let's start with your perception of what Mardi Gras is and means to the public.

You call it a "papier-mâché extravaganza" filled with "rolling toys" that is the "epitome of excess." This supposedly coming from a "New Orleans native."

It reminds me of a recent letter to the editor from a National Guardsman who also assumed an anti-Mardi Gras stance. He said it sends a bad message to hold an event that is nothing more than an excuse to "vomit on Bourbon Street." Just like you, this writer said he was a native, from Slidell.

And, apparently, that gives the both of you free reign to dry hump us while we sleep.

"Hey, you're all fucking morons! But I'm from New Orleans so it's ok! I was born where you now live so that gives me the right to savage your 16-year-old daughter in your newborn's crib! We're family!"

Since you're a native I shouldn't have to explain to you what Mardi Gras means to the people of New Orleans, but it appears as if you've gone simple since moving north.

And that makes me sad. It makes me sad that, as a "New Orleans native," you are under the impression that Mardi Gras is nothing more than a parade of "rolling toys."

But I suppose it doesn't come as a surprise. There are people like you everywhere, the type who move into the French Quarter, carefully arrange their figurines on ancient oak mantles, fix themselves a spot of tea, ease into a $5,000 leather chair and settle in for a quiet night, when, to their horror, they hear music outside their window! And people laughing! And singing! The godless heathens! So they fumble through their pockets for their cell phones, hands trembling with rage, and dial 911, demanding that the police arrest them all! Every last one of those goddamn noise-makers! The next call is to their councilman. "I didn't move into the French Quarter to have my tea time interrupted by music and laughter! Shut down those clubs or I'll chop off your dog's head! The Laughter, it burns my ears!" Moving on to the next point........

You say that Mardi Gras is going to be held because of a "few rich guys with an endowed sense of entitlement."

Now, I'm all for bashing rich guys, though I have the balls to be specific when I do it, unlike you. What you meant was rich, WHITE guys.

But you're sadly misinformed if you think that only rich, white guys want a Mardi Gras this year or that only rich, white guys enjoy Mardi Gras. Shit man, have you ever been to a parade? It ain't just rich, white guys out there. In fact, if a brawl broke out and it was the rich, white guys against everyone else--the rich, white guys would now be an extinct species in New Orleans.

So there's that.

And here's this.

Just about everybody who is living in New Orleans, who has chosen to weather this awful madness, who has opted to support their city, wants a Mardi Gras. That means both blacks and whites. We need something to take our minds off of the death and misery that surrounds us.

Would you rather we sit at home and cry every fucking night? Should we cancel Jazz Fest as well? Should we cancel French Quarter Fest and

Satchmo Fest? How about the St. Patrick's Day Parade? Is it ok if we laugh openly in public?

Do you realize we actually had the nerve to celebrate Halloween? Yeah man, it was a kick. We headed out into the great New Orleans night and did our dirty thing on Decatur Street. It was a blast but I suppose that too was sending the wrong message, right? And God knows we don't want to do that.

We don't want to piss off the moral majority or precious hearts such as your own.

So I suppose we should pretend to be something we're not? Something we never were and hopefully will never be?

We should put our heads down, hold our hands behind our backs, and shuffle quietly through the remainder of our post-Katrina lives.

That's what you want, right?

But you've been gone awhile and in case you've forgotten, New Orleanians pride themselves on not giving a shit about how the rest of the country views us. We like being outcasts.

So fuck how people perceive us. And fuck sending the right message.

Now, if you're talking about sending the wrong message to the thousands of displaced New Orleanians, then I'll listen. I can only imagine how heartbreaking it will be for them to see images of Mardi Gras on a dusty TV screen in a hotel in Idaho or Gary, Indiana. I can imagine how it will tear them apart, how it may seem as if the city is moving on, that they have been forgotten. I know if I lost everything, if my whole life had been destroyed, and I couldn't afford or find a way to come home, my heart and soul would be in pieces.

But I would also hope that for them, seeing Mardi Gras go on in the face of all this destruction, to see the spirit of New Orleans rise from the ashes, that it would give them hope.

But not you.

You worry that "parades will tie up city streets."

Jesus man, get some perspective.

Tie up city streets? Have you been back to New Orleans since Katrina? There's a fifth of the population back. So how in the hell will we be tying up the streets? Why would it tie up the streets now any worse than before the storm?

Mardi Gras fucking justifies the existence of streets in this wasteland. And do you realize how badly the dying businesses along the parade route need the money that Mardi Gras will bring in?

You have about as much knowledge of post-Katrina New Orleans as that fat, junkie-fucking hophead Rush Limbaugh.

You worry about holding Mardi Gras "even as the masses try to make sense of everyday life."

I'm trying to figure out if you could have been any more patronizing or condescending in that last sentence. And I'm coming up empty.

Do you think we're children who can't walk and chew gum at the same time? We're not sitting around like monkeys, scratching our heads and grunting, dumbfounded by these strange, new surroundings, screeching towards dark corners with our hands flailing in the air when that strange orbital light appears in the night sky.

Not only have we "made sense" of our surroundings, we have adapted and are living our lives as best we can.

So don't speak for us or talk down to us or think you have the right to say what is best for us.

You are not here.

Let me repeat--You are not here.

But that don't stop you.

No way. Not you.

You go on to say that you "don't think the citizens are psychologically ready to handle" the crowds that come with Mardi Gras.

Take your dime store psychoanalysis and shove it up your ass.

After what we went through, you think we can't handle some Mardi Gras crowds?

Christ, I don't think you realize how tired we are of people on the outside speaking for us and telling us what is best for us and what we are and are not capable of.

Many years ago you chose to leave New Orleans. And now you hate yourself for it. You hate the fact that you are not here on the ground, experiencing what we are experiencing. So now you are going out of your way to let everyone know that you too are from New Orleans. And you want everyone to know that, as an expert on New Orleans, in your opinion, we are fucking it all up.

And that gives you satisfaction.

From your safe, pristine suburban home, the figurines perfectly aligned on the mantle, you tap your keys with deliberative purpose, picturing yourself down here in the swamp with us, bravely leading us dumb brutes towards salvation, if only somebody would listen.

So everyone knows that you are from New Orleans and that you too are suffering the psychic wounds of your old home.

Good on you man. You just got yourself a little bit of Katrina cred.

Either way, we're going to do whatever the fuck we want and what we want to do is celebrate Carnival.

Sorry Lovell. You didn't think some half-assed editorial from a mouth-breathing hack in Indiana was going to mean a damn, did you?

Poor guy. It really has been a long time since you lived here.

Oh well, come February the streets of New Orleans will be in full-costumed swing, awash in krewes and sin and we will all be better for it.

Sincerely,

Richard A. Webster

Sadly, Mr. Beaulieu refused to allow me to reprint his response. At first he was dismissive, but I egged him on with follow-up emails....

December 12, 2005
Mr. Beaulieu--

True writers revel in the fiery back and forth--Hemmingway, Twain, Fitzgerald, Kerouac, Bukowski, Thompson.

When they received the backhanded backslap in print they returned in kind because it gave them the opportunity to flex their literary muscles.

I was hoping you would back up your opinion with an equally rabid response.

Your "alternative Iowa" crack was a promising start--at least you showed a spine. But then you inhaled your own testicles and bailed.

The difference between you and me? I read the entirety of your piece and responded to your each and every muddled point. Take pride in the fact that your ideas drove me to impale squirrels and smoke mountains of crack.

You had an effect.

I tend not to read pieces that reinforce my beliefs. Soaking in the opposition is the only way to live. That is the sign of a writer and an active and virile mind.

I'll go ahead and assume you're not even reading these words as your practice is to avoid confrontation and the lashings of madmen.

I adopted a one month old boxer puppy from the LASPCA, brought her home, made a nice bed out of swaddling clothes and stabbed her in the spine with a steak knife.

Did you make it that far through this rant or did you flap your limp wrists in the air and scream, "My pride! My terrible wounded pride!"

Just a test.

In closing, eat some Jimson root and manufacture yourself a set of balls.

To shrink from the written word, to shrink from outrage inspired by your own words defeats the point of being a writer.

You'd be best to put down the pen, smash the keyboard with your atrophied claws and run headlong into traffic because you ain't cut out for the literary world.

Your friend and admirer,

Richard Webster

December 12, 2005
Mr. Beaulieu--

Good on you man. I knew you had it in you to fire back in defense of your inflammatory words which you wrote full knowing that they would enrage that segment of the New Orleans population you so specifically targeted.

I hold no ill will towards anybody who stands up to the wild-eyed rants of unknown yet volatile sadists on the other side of the screen.

Your initial one-sentence response really had me on the edge of despair, that someone who held such deep convictions, who was willing to detonate them in the middle of a city-wide funeral march would shrink like a goddamn reformed masochist when suitably attacked.

As for your response, thanks for the tip on Breslin. I never heard of the guy before but did some research and will promptly rush out to the bombed-out remnants of our bookstores and seek out a copy of his work.

As for the rest of your email, I am beginning to take comfort in the defensive and confusing nature of your insecurity.

For instance, how can I "ignore the veracity" of what I am saying? Is that possible?

At one point you claim that what I am saying has truth in it and yet you say I am ignoring my own truth?

Does that make me some sort of schizophrenic savant?

As for your adherence to respecting moral clarity which you equate with respecting other people's opinions.....it's bullshit. You say I failed to meet those qualifications but go back and reread your editorial that ran in the Picayune. It was filled with language that denigrated anyone who held Mardi Gras in high esteem. You threw out any number of playground insults to make your point. And don't get me wrong, I have no problem with playground insults as I'm sure you have come to realize. But don't place yourself on some Valhalla plain of purity and acceptance.

You obviously have your own issues which you are dealing with. And you obviously have your own rage issues.

You called me an angry man. Goddamn right I'm an angry man. I am a furiously enraged man. I am pissed-off and rightly so. And instead of pretending I'm not I have chosen to embrace my anger and become proactive and reactive.

Whatever.

I am active unlike many people around me who talk a good game over beers at the bar. But when they sober up the next day they descend into the typical torpor that has created a frozen generation of TV-zombies and politically stunted fools.

Anger is an underestimated and under-appreciated emotion.

I would advise you to embrace your own. Besides our love for this great city, anger is the only thing that is going to affect change.

Truth to power, right?

Exactly. And don't think I didn't notice how you let your anger seep through in your nasty little dig about the boxer puppy being too smart to get into the car with me. Truth be told, the attempted insult was rather weak but it was an honest reaction. Next time don't hold back.

Fire away man like you did in your editorial. That was full of pure vitriol and rage. You may posture yourself to be some kind of reserved intellectual but you threw me in a full-frothing rage and that takes true talent.

And I'm not talking about the reactionary hate-vomit of people like Hannity, Limbaugh and O'Reilly. They're no better than the bitter drunks with spider-vein noses at the end of the bar waiting for some warm body to enter their time zone so they can roll out glorious chestnuts like, "Democrats suck."

You hit a chord because we are both passionate about the well-being of New Orleans. You hit a chord because while I vehemently disagreed with your take on Mardi Gras, I agreed with your take on the disparity between the poor and the rich, white and black in New Orleans. But you're minimizing the issue by looking at it through the prism of Mardi Gras.

It's symbolic and I don't shine to symbolism.

Talk about housing and our rotten public school system and the lack of opportunity for inner-city youths, but don't waste your time on Mardi Gras. It's like bitching about the statue of General Lee in Lee Circle. It gets press but it doesn't get anyone anywhere.

A shadow puppet. A substitute for flesh and substance.

As for your bizarre references to constantly being dumped into the "animal kingdom".......well man, that's some weird hang-up you and a saucy little therapist are going to have to work out in a dark room on

a red velvet couch, holding hands and primal-screaming all of your cares away.

You asked why people such as myself tend to associate people such as yourself with genitalia and animals?

That's just too fucking weird a question for me to even attempt to answer. Who are people "such as myself?" And who are people "such as yourself?" If you're suggesting these insults of mine are racially motivated, you're way off. My venom is color-blind. It is universal and glorious in its precision.

It is exact and unyielding and knows no bounds.

Before Katrina it was a force but after, well......I myself may need a few hours in the red room with the needle-punchers and fishnet stocking starlets of psychotherapy.

"God endures, wine preserves and the whores blow on."
Charles Bukowski.

Yours in Pabst Blue Ribbon--

Richard Webster

* * * * * * * * *

One London paper proved especially humorous in its coverage of Mardi Gras when it spotlighted Krewe de Vieux, a notoriously obscene and political foot parade through the French Quarter. The writer described how the locals lined the streets drinking hurricanes and openly smoking marijuana in front of a nonplussed police force.

First off, locals don't drink hurricanes unless we're entertaining friends at Pat O'Brien's. You'll concede and have one to take part in the tourista merriment. But then it's straight to beer or shots of tequila and turpentine. We don't drink hurricanes and we don't drink Hand Grenades. That's for the tourists, an easily identifiable marker, like a tag in the ear or a brand on the ass.

We're professional drunks, for good or ill, mostly ill, like that time I threw up on that Quarter bartender.

But sometimes for good, like that time I threw up on that Quarter bartender.

As for smoking marijuana openly in front of the NOPD. Bullshit. You even bump into an NOPD cop nowadays and you'll be face down on the pavement with an elephant's knee jammed in your back. You light a joint in front of them, that's a fucking challenge and one they are not likely to overlook.

But I could be wrong. Maybe we locals did pack Frenchmen and Decatur streets while power-puffing joints in the face of the NOPD brutes. Hell, the writer failed to mention how we sucked on baby bottles filled with LSD and snorted rails of blow off of baby bonnets worn by baby dolls packed with uppers and downers. I myself had a cop hold my camera while I injected heroin into my right armpit because my left is saved for Dilaudid and speedballs.

Yeah, that's what we're about. Nutty fucking druggers and wasters.

Being in the glare of the worldwide press is an interesting phenomenon in that you come to realize how the outside world views you, all of the preconceived notions. Little effort is expended to uncover the truth.

"Oh those dirty New Orleanians, truly they are a besotten people with no regard for any-thing beyond drenching their organs in inebriates and clouding their lungs with the stony, rolling highs. Oh mama! Truly what a scene--enough to bleach your pantyhose. The id of the United States and that terrible ego brought down by a hubris that has led them to believe their organs possess the unique ability to regenerate and multiply on demand."

And I'll milk gin out of my own nipples if that red-faced Brit wasn't hitting up every stoner on that parade route for a hit on a joint or a pull on one of those Hurricanes. After which he retired to the nearest Bourbon Street strip club where he jacked it off under a corner table as he eyeballed the sassy young lassies grinding their finely toned and honed assies on each other.

"Oh mama. Oh mama. God save the Queen. I got it bad for New Orleans. I got it bad for New Orleans. She's trying to kill me. Send two shillings and three pence post-haste or your dearest and only lad will fall prey to the luscious advances of the harlots of this outpost of human rot."

The next batch of Mardi Gras parades kick off this Thursday and as opposed to the first tame weekend the second and final weekend will surely prove to be a blitzkrieg on my liver and kidney and heart and psyche. There is no way to properly prepare, though I have been in training since I moved here in 1998. It's impossible to protect yourself. All you can do is go with it and by the end hope that you have a few friends left to vouch for your good name.

This will be the cleansing time. Any demons you got will be properly disposed of or handed the keys to the operation. At this point it's out of our hands. And if it's true that God hates New Orleans, then this is our revenge. Or the undeniable proof of our guilt. Watch the television closely for signs of our ultimate demise or predestined victory. If we make it out of this, then anthropologists should categorize a new classification of people known as the Indestructible Cretins of the Crescent.

Mistake our smiles for the dimwitted children of the basin at your own peril.

We're whistling a new tune

We're starting to feel just fine.

Don't worry about us no more.

We're back to being on the drunk side of fine.

Everyone has an opinion about New Orleans, how we should act, what we should do and how deep we should feel. It's an uncomfortable position for a people who savor their independence from the union. But here we are, the target of editorials and opinion columnists and bitch-tit radio whores like Limbaugh and O'Reilly who removed his newly purchased four-pronged, egg-beating anal vibrator long enough to thrash our corpses for the glory of his ego.

This is what he had to say about the people who chose not to evacuate:

"Many, many, many of the poor in New Orleans are…substance abusers, they're mentally ill, they're screwed up, they can't carry on a conversation, they're catatonic, they're schizophrenic….They weren't going to leave no matter what you did. They weren't going to get turned off from their source. They were thugs, whatever."

But hey big boys, we can take it. No worries. Even in death we got a sense of humor and a real sense of our proper doom. It's wonderful to be alive or dead having known what it meant to spend long nights stumbling down Decatur on Mardi Gras Day with a plastic bag sagging heavy with the weight of eight 16-ounce cans of Budweiser, trippin' on ecstasy, dressed like rabbits with pink fuzzy tails, hopping down the boozy trail in search of the noble Orgy of the Hare that typically kicks it on Frenchmen Street round-about Café Brasil.

And that's what we did. We lived our lives. We did what New Orleanians do. We got fitted in Mad Hatter costumes and got drunk and mocked everything you stand for. But more importantly, we celebrated everything that this city believes in.

"Yeah, we know what those anti-American liberals in Scum City believe in," belched the right-wing, radio-hate operators. "They believe in self-gratification and Parisian excess. They believe in welfare and public handouts and free drugs for elementary school children. And above all else, they believe in man before God. That's why that hurricane chose them. That's why their city lies in ruins, because they deserved it."

And then O'Reilly turned off his mic and launched himself on his assistant, begging her to suck on his neck flap while he lathered up a loofah with salsa and meerkat pheromones.

At the same moment, more than 1,000 miles south in Florida, Limbaugh stole away from his EIB studio, directing his limo driver to the parking lot of a run-down burger stand in Ft. Lauderdale where he traded a 2-year-old black baby from New Orleans for 7,000 Oxycontin pills.

"There's more dark meat where that came from!" he screamed before dissolving into a puddle of urine and narcotic drool.

Well done honorable Americans. And while you go about your patriotic duties, let me spell out what the people of New Orleans believe in.

We do believe in self-gratification.
We do believe in Parisian excess.
And some of us do believe in the sporadic benefits of drug use.
But those are the more obvious tenets of our faith system.
And though this may surprise you, they are the lesser of our beliefs.
Above all else, we believe in each other.
We believe in our congregations that form from the dust in sweltering streets behind tubas and trombones.
We believe in the sermons delivered from honey vocal chords.
We believe in the healing power of friendly faces, newly scarred and traced with familiar tears.
But above all, above anything else, we believe in New Orleans.
Now more than ever.

Many lost, foggy weeks later:
Thank Christ. Mardi Gras is over. As is St. Patrick's Day which we split into two weekends of parades and mass gatherings of serious raucous sots and lushes.
I'll refrain from recounting the depravity of it all. For one, I don't remember much. Two, I choose not to relive what I remember. Best to move on.

But there is little time for rest during this time in New Orleans known affectionately as the Gauntlet. Just as Mardi Gras ends, St. Patrick's Day begins followed by the French Quarter Fest and then Jazz Fest. After that it's the long, terrible, skin-melting summer and the beginning of the hurricane season.

How many days do we got?

June 1st kicks it off.

Shit. We still haven't scraped the dust of Katrina off our sneaker soles. They sit on the back stoop like some terrible reminder we're afraid to toss in the trash.

But not me.

After I got stuck in the mud in Gentilly in a truck driven by a Marine who made a bad decision and a worse turn, just a few weeks after Katrina when bodies were still tied to telephone poles, I took off my pants and sneakers and socks and tossed those fuckers in the garbage and never looked back.

Though it seems that's all I do these days.

Look back.

Constantly thinking back to those days.

And the weeks that followed.

Katrina is everywhere.

Ninth Entry:
Mar23ch 2006,

Rat
Whore
Motherfuckers

IT'S ONLY BEEN 5 MONTHS SINCE IT ALL WENT TO SHIT.
WE HAVE NO IDEA WHAT TYPE OF CITY WE WILL BE LIVING
IN IN ONE YEAR'S TIME. BUT IF THESE ARE CLUES, WELL,
I MAY SWITCH TO TEQUILA BREAKFASTS FOR THE LONG HAUL.
WAFFLES AND GIN SYRUP TOPPED WITH A FINE WHITE POWDER.

There was a story in the Picayune about how the forced exodus of New Orleans dealers and street thugs has opened the doors for the worst of the national and international gangs. The town is ripe for a takeover. The times they are a changin'. Even the faces of the fuckers who will be robbing and killing and raping us will soon be unrecognizable. Prior to the hurricane, according to the FBI, these international gangs tried to infiltrate New Orleans but our suicidal, "who gives a shit if we live another five minutes" boys-on-the-block drove them out the backdoors with Glocks blazin' in all directions. Those motherfuckin' New Orleans rollers are some scary children of inherent violence, too much for even the worst the world has to offer.

When I heard that piece of history it filled me with a warped sense of pride. Even if these murderous children have proven to be a curse, they're our curse and these days civic pride is at an all-time high.

So come on back boys and do that thing you do so well. Set your psychotic minds on rampage and get after 'dem Latin Kings and 'dat MS-13 with their pretty machetes.

And when you're done with them, unfortunately, our partnership will come to an end and it will be back to our respective trenches.

But you dumb little fuckers can't even get with the plan, can you? You've started to return in small packs. But instead of taking care of the invading hordes you've reverted to your pre-Katrina thumb-sucking ways and targeted your fellow storm survivors, we the easy marks.

* * * * * * * *

NO crime resurgence unsettling
By Richard A. Webster New Orleans CityBusiness Staff Writer

April 8, 2006 -- Just before midnight on a Sunday in mid-February, 18 people were throwing back beers in Parasol's, the popular Irish Channel bar, when two young men crashed through the front door.

One, his face obscured by a bandana, pointed an assault rifle at the startled crowd while the other, T-shirt pulled over his mouth and nose, threatened them with a semiautomatic pistol.

They ordered the bartender to empty the register and everyone else to pull out their wallets and cash.

Parasol's owner Jeffrey Carreras said the armed thieves stuffed several thousand dollars into their pockets and walked a few blocks down the street, guns held casually by their sides, to where they parked their car.

"One guy got in the driver's seat, let his partner in, started up the car and then had to back up and move forward several times like they had parallel-parked before they could even get out," Carreras said. "It was the first time we've been robbed in about six years."

News of the Parasol's robbery quickly spread throughout the close-knit Uptown bar community.

"What scares me is if they come to take money it's one thing. But nowadays sometimes it's not enough to give them your money. They may want to shoot you anyway," said Steve Watson, owner of the Kingpin on Lyons and Prytania streets. "It's depressing because most people who own bars know each other. We're all supportive of each other and if it can happen to Parasol's it can happen to anybody."

The Parasol's incident is a cautionary tale to bartenders who work late nights and walk with hundreds of dollars in cash. It reminds them the crime-free days following Hurricane Katrina--when National Guardsmen strapped with M-16s patrolled the streets--are officially over.

"You might take it for granted that things are good and everyone is safe and then something like that happens to remind us that there are bad people out there doing bad things," said Steve Peterson, owner of the Rendezvous bar on Magazine Street. "People got robbed before the storm, and then there was a lull and it looked like things had gotten a lot better, and now it seems to be coming back."

New Orleans Police Department Superintendent Warren Riley said there was a small spike in crime following Mardi Gras but rates are down overall. "Before the storm we were getting our behinds kicked even though we were doing all we could. But we're at the point now where crime is way down and this city has the opportunity to turn around," Riley said. "Mardi Gras came and we believe that a lot of our bad element came back into town and didn't leave because the spike began right after Mardi Gras. We had a problem location Uptown by the former St. Thomas development, which we've effectively shut down, and now we're focused on areas in Carrollton and Algiers."

Kimble Donnington-Smith, a bartender at the Balcony Bar on Magazine Street, said he feels well protected in a high-traffic area but is not immune from the return of violent crime.

Two weeks ago an unknown assailant mugged a young woman three blocks from the Balcony.

"I'm becoming more aware of just crime in general going on around the city, like what happened in the Marigny," Donnington-Smith said, referring to the March 18 mugging and murder of 28-year-old Michael Frey in the 2100 block of Chartres Street.

"That's just shocking; the worst kind of death," Donnington-Smith said. "Somebody shot like that seems absolutely senseless."

Bar owners install security cameras and hire doormen but they don't want to turn their businesses, which people frequent to escape daily pressures, into maximum-security fortresses.

"After something like that happens you're uptight and start looking at people differently but there's always been crime in this city. When your time comes, your time comes," said Carreras. "We're armed and well lit outside so it was pretty ballsy of those kids to storm in here like that. But we're a friendly, local bar and we're not going to change the nature of our business because then we'll be giving into them. We have a buzzer on our door. It just so happens that on that night we got lackadaisical about using it."

At the Half Moon in the Lower Garden District, manager Sarah Harkins said the main concern is the return of the pre-hurricane population of "hookers and crackheads."

"Right after the storm, between October and December, there were no hookers or crackheads, and then in January all of a sudden they're back," Harkins said. "We have three crack houses within two blocks around us and our biggest problem is trying to keep them out and away from our sidewalk because they're hurting our business. Sometimes all I do is nothing but bounce hookers and crackheads."

Another problem Harkins said, involves Hispanic workers.

"Our biggest problem with the Latino dudes is they have no IDs, half are illegal and they drink so much they start fights. I've had two knife fights since we reopened."

Donnington-Smith said the Balcony Bar has had several run-ins with Hispanic laborers.

"A lot are armed and a lot of them like to drink so you have to tread carefully. One time we had a guy at the cigarette machine, when he reached down to grab his pack a gun fell out of his pocket."

Harkins credits the Sixth District police for eliminating her fear of being robbed at gunpoint.

"The police keep pretty good tabs on us throughout the night," Harkins said. "There's even a Sixth District bike patrol in a six-block radius around us so they're really making an effort to clean up this area. I never really get concerned. My customers are more concerned than me. They think I'm crazy but I've never waited longer than two minutes to get a response from the cops."

Carreras said the incident at Parasol's has been used to symbolize the return of violent crime in New Orleans but cautions about reading too much into it.

"I was in Italy taking a break from everything and I was reading the International Herald. There was a story about the crime rate going back up in New Orleans and five *paragraphs in they mentioned Parasol's getting robbed. But crime has always existed in New Orleans. Nothing much has changed."*

* * * * * * * * *

It's only been 5 months since it all went to shit. We have no idea what type of city we will be living in in one year's time. But if these are clues, well, I may switch to tequila breakfasts for the long haul. Waffles and gin syrup topped with a fine white powder.

Last week the city began demolishing houses deemed unsalvageable in the Ninth Ward. A few days ago the cops raided Lee Circle where the day-laborers hang out in the parking lot of the gas station waiting for contractors in pick-up trucks to roll by with offers of a day's work. The police threw out a net and arrested 40 illegals but their real targets were the members of the El Salvador gangs that have been tagging buildings with their MS-13 markings.
And the march of death keeps coming.
Insatiable.
On my birthday, I found out Steve, who I knew through my friend Jerry Bob, overdosed, a few months after Katrina. He always had problems. Tortured by a lost love that sent him into a black spiral.
I'm not saying it had anything to do with the storm. But it happened and it leaves me thinking.
Before the storm, maybe the shock of hearing about a friend overdosing would have been more profound. But now, it hits with a familiar feeling, a sad shake of the head and a moment of silence.

Poor fucking bastard.
Who's next?
Adam.
That's who.
Adam was an old drunk who I knew vaguely from the Avenue.
The story, as told by second-hand sources, goes like this: Adam returned home after a long day of drinking. It was around 8 p.m. He lived on the second floor of a St. Charles house. Apparently, a crew of construction workers was banging away on the building and Adam got pissed and asked them to kill the noise. Now here is where the tale gets murky. The first slant I heard was that the contractors picked Adam up and tossed him off the balcony. Emergency Medical Services took him to the hospital where he died a short time after.

Some are now saying maybe he fell or that they just pushed him and he broke through the balcony and fell to his death. Who knows? Only the contractors and they ain't admitting shit.

Peek-a-Boo Paul, the Lilliputian racist, said Adam had previously fallen off the balcony. So maybe that's what happened; only this time he didn't survive the fall.

And yeah, Peek-a-Boo Paul and his racist elfin cohort Suds are back in the Avenue, the owner having lifted their suspensions.

Come one come all. No hard feelings. The Avenue doesn't discriminate against black-hating dwarves.

And I think to myself what a wonderful world.

And then I go to Walgreens to get the paper and the cashier asked the two young black kids in front of me whether they were going to the second line.

"We just came from there and we ain't goin' back," one said. "Somebody got shot. We got the hell out of there."

The cashier, a young woman, didn't seem overly fazed. "People in N'awlins just can't get along," she said.

Two people shot. One died. 19 years old.

We're settling back into our old ways.

A friend of Joe the barback at the Balcony was shot to death in the Marigny last weekend. Some kid held him up and after he handed over his wallet the kid blasted him in the chest. Gather en masse to mourn death and celebrate life and maybe take out a few more un-lucky motherfuckers.

I'm not saying I'm living in a frontier city trying to get a grip on this thing called civiliza-tion. I'm just describing what it's like to live in a place where hundreds of thousands of houses are blacked-out, gutted and dead, where people have taken to blocking off high-ways with pick-up trucks so they can personally ask those wishing to enter their part of town what their business is in order to prevent looters from creeping and crawling in their neighborhoods.

We're trying to revamp our political structure and model of government.

We're trying to reestablish normal trash pick-up and something resembling a dependable mail service.

Forty percent of our traffic lights are inoperable.

What else?

What more?

Or less?

Suicides have doubled.

How about that?

Incest and domestic violence are on the rise.

The homeless population jumps by the day.

Weird shit.

And then there's this, what happened a few days before Fat Tuesday……

A young couple was walking home from the Mardi Gras parades, just a few blocks from the Balcony Bar in Uptown where my friends and I spend most of our nightly hours.

As the couple approached their home, a black pick-up tore through a red light.

The husband yelled for the truck to slow down.

A natural reaction.

His wife walked up the steps to their apartment as her husband lagged behind.

She said she saw the black truck reappear from around the corner.

She said she saw it pick up speed.

Her husband pointed at the truck and said, "There's that crazy guy again."

He smiled at his wife.

Her loving husband, strands of Mardi Gras beads around his neck.

She smiled back.

She loved him.

She said she saw the truck reappear from around the corner.

She said she heard the roar of the engine as it barreled towards her husband.

Stupid drunks.

Don't they have anything better to do then try to scare good, honest people?

Was it really so bad that someone told them to slow down, to cut the gas so as not to endanger the little tricycle-ridin' kiddies?

Was that so wrong?

What got under their skin?

What was in their blood?

But it's the crazy season, right?

It's Mardi Gras and drunk people do the things drunk people do, even when behind the wheel of a 4,500-pound block of steel.

He was always looking out for others, her husband, her love.

She said she didn't have time to react.

That black pick-up truck that reappeared after her husband yelled at it to slow down, it didn't swerve or lose control.

It took aim, spotlighted its target and pulled the trigger.

It bounced over the curb, burned through two lanes of traffic, ran over her husband and sped off.

The man behind the wheel of the black pick-up truck couldn't let something like that go, some prissy little family man shouting at him to slow the fuck down, to have some human decency.

Who the fuck did he think he was?

Thinking he's a better man, barking orders like the rest of them.

Happy little prick with his tight-ass college bitch.

Fuck that.

"You know what you should do?"

What?

"Run that fucker over."

Do what?

"You heard me. Time to kill."

Jesus. I've done too much meth. I'm hallucinating.

"No. You're thinking straight for the first time."

My goddamn brain.

So you want me to plow into that little wretch?

"Quick! Turn around the block. There he is. You see him?"

Yeah.

"Run that motherfucker over. Don't scare him. Kill him. Destroy him. Fuck that bitch. Make her watch as we smash his bones and take away everything she cares about. Take it all away. Make her pay. Make him taste pain. And then blood. And then nothing."

Yeah. Fuck him. I'm gonna kill that bastard. No one tells me what to do.

"Except for me."

Right. Except for you.

"They think Katrina hurt? How 'bout some fucking chrome and rubber? Fuck this city."

Yeah.

Kill'em all.

Wild, Wild West.

Old school car death.

He never saw it coming.

They never do.

They never expect the bloodlust.

They never anticipate the monstrous.

And yet never have a people been more prepared, more conditioned for the horrifying uprising of nature and the failings of mankind.

132

And yet, still, these lovely southern children of tragedy refuse to see it, expecting the best when the worst has littered their home with the remains of thousands.
And that makes it all so easy.

They said he was a wonderful husband.
She said the truck was black.
They said the husband and wife loved Mardi Gras.
She said the driver was white, middle-aged.
They said it was a tragedy.
She collapsed.
They said it was awful.
They shook their heads.
And she disappeared into the darkness of her home, their home.

I drive by that intersection every day.
It's just another intersection.
Another unmarked grave.
Hundreds pass through it,
Pass through the ghost of the fallen man,
Who remains on the corner
Searching for his wife,
With a bag of Mardi Gras beads in his hand,
Lost and lonely,
Confused and disturbed.
"Where is my beloved wife?"
"Where is my home?"
"Where is my love?"
"My love!"

New Orleans is a city of ghosts, a newly cursed town of nightmares where the whispers of dark memories find purchase in the minds of the lost and pained.
Not everyone can hear them. Most refuse. Most shut them out, barricading their souls with reason and a hardened determination to forever look forward, and never back.
Never look back.
Never think of the things that occurred in the hellish days that brought us all to this wretched reality.
Never allow those memories to seep into precious sanity.
And don't you ever pay any fucking attention to the ghosts on the corner.
They do not exist.
There are no ghosts.

There is only the recovery and rebuilding and commerce and the future.

And that noise, the soft gurgling whimpers of what sounds like a little girl gasping for life, up there in the attic, clawing at the walls, moaning for her mother, her mommy, her momma—it's not real.

There are no ghosts.

They do not exist.

Not to you anyway.

But to us, to the fuck-ups, to the emotionally unstable, the ones with their brains opened wide, we can't help but see and hear and feel them. All them ghosts, all them afterlife pleas for assistance and salvation.

It plagues us because we can't help but believe.

We lack the defenses to shield us from the deathly howling that echoes from tomb to tourniquet.

We are raw and exposed.

By choice.

I want to see the hallowed eyes of the dead peering through my bedroom window in that unnerving time between unconsciousness and reality when it all seems to come tumbling down.

I want to hear their desperate cries beneath the blare of a dirty dive jukebox. While the chronic drunks are bobbing their heads to the Stooges, I want to have my head cocked, ears to the wind, bombarded by the unanswered prayers of all of those people, the mothers and fathers and children and the ones in-between, who believed in dreams and the possibilities of life, that magic was not a fool's endeavor, that the incredible was possible.

I would rather be haunted by the impossible misgivings of the dead than the mindless ignorance of the living.

I don't want to forget.

I don't want to move forward.

I don't want to get well.

I want to bury myself in the past, in those Katrina days.

And I don't know why.

It's not healthy and it's not sane.

It's not natural and it's not normal.

But I can't let go.

I can't summon the strength to abandon this pain of mine.

It's all I got.

And if I let it drift into the abyss, what will I be left with?

A shell of a life and a mini-mall and microwave popcorn and an alarm clock and the TV Guide that will dictate the remaining hours of my life.

Life?

I don't think so.

So I choose to hold tight to my pain for the wonder of the busload of gawkers that have descended on our coast, faces pressed deep into the window panes of the buses that crawl by as tour guides point out specific traits that have come to mark our kind.

"Now, if you look closely at that man there, in front of his decimated home, you can almost make out a touch of murderous rage beneath his zombie pallor. Can you see it?"

"I see it!" an old woman screams, jabbing her husband holding the camera to take a picture.

"And here on our left is what seems to be a small child. But upon closer inspection you can see that there is no 'child' left in this boy. Who knows what horrors he experienced during the storm! But whatever torment he endured, you can see that it sucked his soul dry. He may as well be a geriatric or a dead-eyed serial killer."

"Simply wonderful," gasps an anthropologist from New York.

Tourism is the lifeblood of New Orleans and so long as people are bleeding that industry will thrive.

* * * * * * * *

Guides stand behind controversial 'Catastrophe Tour'
By Richard A. Webster New Orleans CityBusiness Staff Writer

January 9, 2006 -- Chuck Scroggins lost everything when the floodwaters of Hurricane Katrina rushed into his two-story eastern New Orleans home.

At 65 years old, he is now living with a friend in Faubourg Marigny as he attempts to piece together the remnants of his shattered life.

Julie Gorney spent the past three months trying to salvage the contents of the Slidell home her 83-year-old mother and deceased father bought in 1947.

It is backbreaking work, she said, but worth it if she is able to preserve just a handful of memories of the life her mother once cherished.

Scroggins and Gorney are just two examples of the hundreds of thousands who suffered at the terrible hands of Hurricane Katrina. But some believe they are members of a greedy operation profiting from all the pain and misery.

Scroggins and Gorney are tour guides on Gray Line New Orleans' controversial "Hurricane Katrina — America's Greatest Catastrophe Tour," which held its inaugural run Wednesday.

Sidney Smith, owner of Haunted History Tours, who lost his Mid-City home during the hurricane, says the disaster tour is disturbing.

"I would never even consider the idea of profiting off someone's misery or misfortune," Smith said. *"I have friends in Lakeview and they're really appalled by the whole idea."* Gorney sees it differently.

"We've been accused of profiting off other people's pain but it's not other people's pain — it's our people and our pain," Gorney said. *"It's a New Orleans story told by New Orleanians. Yet people on the outside, especially the national press, are trying to decide what the folks on the inside should be talking about. That's not fair. They don't know what we've been through."*

The three-hour Catastrophe Tour begins at the foot of Canal Street and hits many of the somber landmarks of Hurricane Katrina — the Superdome, Charity Hospital and the Ernest N. Morial Convention Center. From downtown it moves to Lakeview where tourists are given their first glimpse of the devastation — 8-foot-high, rust-brown watermarks wrapped around the wooden carcasses of many former homes.

After Lakeview, the tour bus heads to Gentilly covering square mile after square mile of abandoned brick homes, many with small squares of blue tarp tacked to roofs to cover the holes where desperate people hacked their way out of sweltering attics.

Julee Pearce, Gray Line marketing director, said the tour avoids the Ninth Ward because it is not safe or passable in many sections and because they want people to know it was not just poor African-Americans in the Ninth Ward who suffered.

The tour costs $35 per person. Gray Line donates $3 from every ticket to a local charity chosen by the visitor.

Gray Line initially planned one daily run of the Catastrophe Tour but public demand forced it to expand to three on its inaugural day.

Pearce defends the tour, saying it raises awareness by giving outsiders a firsthand view of the devastation and provides much-needed income to the few remaining Gray Line employees.

"We went from 65 to six employees because there's no tour business left in the city," Pearce said. *"These people depended on that salary to pay their rent and house note or to buy clothes and groceries. They were taxpaying citizens and if we can make money to hire those employees back, it will help with the recovery."*

Carol Stauder, 63, is a Catastrophe tour guide. Her Clearview Parkway home in Metairie took on more than a foot of water.

Stauder used to do all the Gray Line tours — the swamp, Lower Garden District and Louisiana Purchase tours — but said the Catastrophe Tour is the only one selling post-Katrina.

"They'll call you the night before you're scheduled to work and say no one's on the walking tour tomorrow so don't come in. So what is Gray Line supposed to do? Be like every business that has fallen on hard times and close up and move to another state? We're

trying to support the economy," Stauder said. "I don't want to get defensive but it really
rubs me the wrong way when people say we're profiteering.
Some of us lost everything like Chuck (Scroggins)."
After losing his home of 21 years, Scroggins said he feared he would also lose his job as
a Gray Line tour guide. He has a pension but said it is not enough to pay his bills.
When Gray Line approached Scroggins about conducting a catastrophe tour, he said he
was apprehensive.
"I love the city so much and it just hurts in my heart to see the devastation," Scroggins
said. "But when I stopped and realized this wasn't anything being done for sensational-
ism or anything else, that the purpose was to educate and inform, I felt it was my duty
to help bring this message to the rest of the nation. We're down on our knees and need
help."

* * * * * * * *

A letter to the honorable Rep. Jeb Hensarling, R-TX, and Sen. Bob Bennett, R-Utah.
Re: Hensarling's comments--"I saw public officials who took very little responsibility
(for failures in responding to the hurricane) and are looking for large checks from the federal government. Where's the plan? Where's the accountability? What is the city doing?
What is the state doing? Those able-bodied individuals under 65, what are they doing to
help themselves?"
And Bennett's comments: "Building a city 10 feet below sea level does not strike me as
inherently, basically a good idea. If someone makes a really stupid decision in the name
of nostalgia that we want to rebuild this neighborhood just like it was, maybe Katrina
said to us, you don't want a neighborhood there."

I would like to thank both of you noble and esteemed gentlemen. I was worrying, in my
private moments, that I was losing the rage and anger that coursed through my veins in
the months immediately following Katrina. I feared I was losing my edge.
Though 80 percent of my city lies in ruins, though hundreds of thousands have been
displaced and police continue to find corpses in the rubble, adding to the pile of dead
already hundreds high, I found myself settling into a strangely comfortable existence,
even if it consists of driving past abandoned and gutted homes with water marks higher
than the bloody skull of Christ. Whatever it is, it is a daily routine and can soothe people
even when they live in the bottom of a burnt crater, pock-marked with the blood of family and friends and the strangers we took for granted, the kind and sometimes cruel faces
we passed on the sidewalks. But many of those people are dead and even more have been
forced from their homes.

But what of it, right? What's a few hundred water-logged negro corpses?

The dumb brutes were too stupid to realize that they were living at the bottom of a 20-foot swimming pool with no ladders, right?

For the moment let's forget about the ugly reality that the swimming pool had supposedly been protected by the U.S. Corps of Engineers. I say supposedly because that protection happened to be made out of stacked cardboard boxes, the holes plugged with the discarded, used condoms more commonly found on the floors in the dark recesses of Congress where honorable men such as yourselves steal away with impressionable young men and women eager to learn the ways of government.

And oh boy do you show them the way, fingers deeply embedded in shoulder blades, grape lollipops shoved in their mouths to muffle their screams.

I don't begrudge you the fun times. After all, what is a democracy without a semen-stained pile of hay for the decision-makers to occasionally roll around in with some warm flesh?

But I digress.

Where was I?

Oh yes. I was talking about the ignorant brutes who lived in the lower Ninth Ward and Gentilly and New Orleans East. Stupid fuckers.

And now, get this congressmen, these towel-snappers actually want the federal government to spend some cash to rebuild their homes that so happened to be demolished by the half-assed levees built by the Corps (i.e. the federal government).

Can you believe that shit?

Don't we give them enough, these lazy, doodle-sucking welfare queens and long-dick baby-makers?

All they ever want is a goddamn handout.

I had forgotten about their craven greed until the two of you plain-spoken sons of whores snapped me back to reality.

Give an inch and they'll ask for free crack.

Where does it stop?

Next thing you know they'll be asking you to rebuild the hospitals and schools that were wiped out when the claymation levees opened wide and let the floodwaters roll.

But that's all recent and painful history.

I am writing to ask for your forgiveness.

Please don't think that everyone in New Orleans shares the same rotten characteristics as these people you hold in such brilliant contempt. Many of us are proud Confederates who look the other way when the guy down the street decides to top off his first marriage with four more Heaven-blessed unions, even if one of them is to his 13-year old cousin (that one was for you Mr. Bennett).

I also want to thank you for kick-starting my rage. For too long I had focused on the trail of scales left behind by Washington politicians who came to witness the carnage of Katrina only to wipe their $4,000 shoes on their way out of our dying city on the bloated corpse of Kenisha Williams, single mother of four.

You have shown me that my anger was misplaced.

I should have been focused on the people of New Orleans who had the nerve to ask for a handout from the cash-starved and fiscally responsible federal government.

Oh my sheep-humping God! Don't they realize that you gentlemen are duty-bound to maintain a steel grip on our national treasure? Do they think that you just toss out wads of cash for any mind-addled adventure that seems to have no end or reason?

And you're right Mr. Hensarling, just what are the able-bodied people under 65 doing to rebuild their homes?

Well, I'll tell you. I'll run down their daily itinerary.

They get up sometime after 1 p.m. at which time they spend a good 23 minutes massaging their genitals with FEMA checks. The ink, I've heard, used on government checks is an especially powerful aphrodisiac. And they get down on those rectangular slabs of paper with fly-flicking tongues as if they were neon-glowing toads.

After that they begin their day.

Mix three quarts of gin with two tablespoons of orange juice, a dime bag of cocaine, four Oxycontins, and retire to the couch. Again, I've been told the high of this particular mixture, commonly referred to as Katrina Juice, makes for an enjoyable afternoon.

Now what happens next depends of the ratio of cocaine to Oxycontin. Should the user go for the 4:1 mix in favor of the coke, well then, it's off to the supermarket for some shoplifting and up-skirt hijinks. If the ratio favors the Oxycontin, well, it's nothing but dreams of Laura Bush in sensible pumps and butt-plugs.

When the sun sets the able-bodied, under-65 crowd congregates in a centrally located house for some baby porn and group sex.

It's my belief that their refusal to lift a hammer to rebuild their shattered homes stems from their need for discreet shelters in bombed-out neighborhoods to get their post-hurricane groove on.

You thought New Orleans was bad before Katrina, well guys, you ain't seen nothin'.

You see Mr. Bennett, for some it's about nostalgia. Some wish to return to the old New Orleans, the place that gave birth to jazz, where the Mardi Gras Indians stomped down the streets and the brass bands led hundreds in spontaneous celebrations of life. They want to revert to the days when they congregated for barbecues in the same neighborhoods where four generations of their families lived and built and owned homes. They wish to return to the 150-year-old churches where their parents wed and their children were baptized. They wish to return and rebuild the businesses that supported their loved ones and neighbors, return to the only home they have ever known.

139

Foolish, blind fucking nostalgia.

They actually want to return to a time when they believed the word of the federal government that the levees were state-of-the-art, that they were well protected from a Category 3 storm, just like Katrina when she rammed into New Orleans.

They don't realize it's just not possible. The country has other priorities like a $286.4 billion transportation bill.

Fix those fucking roads or we're all going to die.

But shit, if the roads and bridges keep breaking down maybe it's God's way of saying we don't need roads and bridges.

If something breaks, fuck it.

That's the great pioneer spirit this country was founded upon.

Of course, there are exceptions, like Iraq. We keep pumping hundreds of billions into that country even though the only thing we have to show for it are thousands of dead soldiers, tens of thousands of dead Iraqis and a government of virgin-mad, pipe-bomb aficionados.

But what do I know? I got my dick stuffed in a severed chicken's head, even as I type this.

It takes me back to the womb.

It's all weird voodoo shit. Please forgive me.

Well, I believe I've taken far too much of your valuable time.

Just know that there are those here in this shattered and dying city of New Orleans who didn't think your comments were the ignorant and racist rantings of two tiny, hateful men with atrophied penises and dark, secret longings to jam their fists into the assholes of the blue-skinned corpses that have long-littered our city just to see what it feels like to be black for a moment in time.

I say have at it boys. Get your chocolate fantasies on and then retire to the pits and cleanse yourselves for it's a long road to the promised land and neither one of you champions of common sense and fiscal sanity has anything to worry about.

God loves a winner and that's why he rolled the dark waters over the soft skulls of the children of New Orleans who made one last lunge for the hands of their desperate mommas before it all went cold and suffocating.

I get where you're coming from.

You're just trying to save us from our own ignorant and blind selves.

Though the people of New Orleans are willing to bleed and starve and bruise every inch of their bodies to preserve and rebuild their beloved city, you know better, kind all-knowing masters that you are.

Every day we are reminded of the dead, their shadows burned on our walls, their dirges ringing out from distant ceremonies. And despite the specter of what has been, we smile and dance and love and stake our claims.

140

This is our city.

You wanna deny us assistance?

Then keep your fucking money.

You think it will stop us from rebuilding, from committing suicide in your eyes?

We got a taste for death now brothers and it no longer scares us.

This is our fucking country and we'll sink into the swamps until the last beer is snatched from the shelf.

This is New Orleans.

You have accused us of being lazy and blinded by nostalgia, greedy money-whores looking to substitute hard work with handouts.

I get it. I get your self-imposed ignorance. But I have a solution.

Next time you visit New Orleans, our private Armageddon, step off the fucking tour bus and sit for a spell with the crippled survivors.

Unlike me, most will not unsheathe their machetes with an eye on your throats. They will place tender hands on your arms as tears drown their eyes. Their hoarse voices will tremble as they describe to you how their hearts came to be tracked with hundreds of inflamed scars.

And then comes the flood of memories—days spent in 100 degree attics, frantic calls to already dead relatives, hallucinations of baby bodies floating past second-story windows. Blood on the walls, screams from down the block. And then the blackout and the hereafter, the fog of post-disaster survival in which we have all existed and continue to exist while people such as yourselves, in the womb of uncorrupted security, tell us to stop acting like welfare queens and two-dollar queers.

And as these people speak, look at the blood on their knuckles that pounded against attic ceilings searching for that soft spot that would lead to a second birth and an extension of life.

Ask them about their family and their future and their pain. Ask them about the absence of hope even as they restack the fallen bricks of long-gone bedroom walls.

You fucking ask them whether they have been living the good life on government handouts, or if they have spent the past six months in hell. Then ask yourselves what it would feel like to have everything taken from you in one, terrible moment. Everything you once knew--your friends, family, house, job, neighborhood, and the pictures and remembrances of generations past. Ask what it feels like to lose the only image you had of your long-dead parents, the framed picture of your mom and dad during the happy times, before the ruin of it all.

Better yet, ask the mother who lost her three children to the storm if she is out for an easy handout.

Better yet, don't ask her. Look into her shell-shocked face and accuse her, as you seem so comfortable doing from the recesses of your Washington D.C. hyperbolic chambers, of being a lazy black strain on the American Dream that you have worked your entire life to uplift and perpetuate.

But you will never do that, will you?

You have no goddamn right to judge us or dismiss what we have endured.

You have no fucking right to question our motives.

But you most likely stopped reading this after the first few paragraphs.

This is your world.

And I suppose it's time for me to get with the program.

So fuck New Orleans.

Fuck the welfare queens and crack addicts.

Fuck the junkies and faggots.

Fuck the babies and mommas and daddies and sistahs and bruthas.

Fuck that goddamned Big Easy.

Fuck them jazz cats and their swinging, ringing horny southern whores.

Fuck'em all.

Let'em fucking burn.

Or drown.

Just die.

Move on.

Fuck New Orleans.

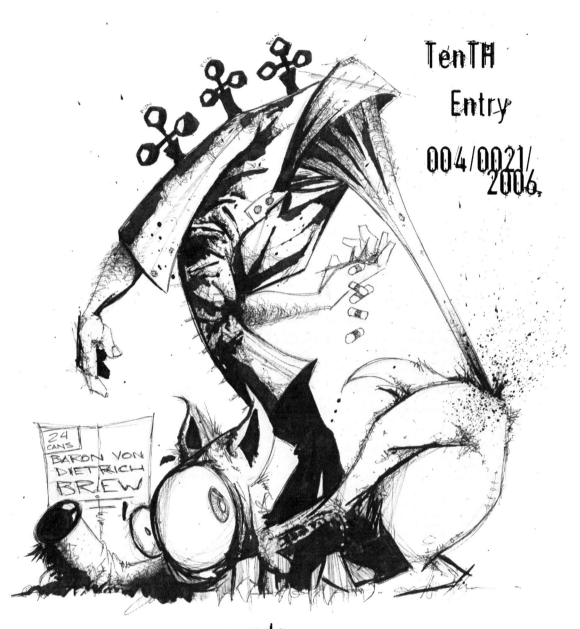

Triumph OF the upturned Turtle Man ....

"I AM NOT WHO YOU THINK I AM!" I SHOUTED.
I AM BUT A REFLECTION OF WHAT OUR KINGMAKER GEORGES

INTENDED! I AM BOTH THE COCKROACH AND TURTLE

THAT TORMENTS AND TEASES YOU IN THE EYES

OF YOUR OWN DREAMY NIGHTMARISH HURRICANES!

LEAVE ME BE AND ONE DAY I WILL RISE AGAIN AND
REVEAL TO YOU THE TRUE FACE OF HUMANITY!"

The first time I set foot in New Orleans was during my junior year in college in 1994. I came with two friends, a glorious drunk and a Chong-smokin' fiend. We took the train from Philly with bad intentions. My obsession with New Orleans started the first time I heard "Gris Gris Gumbo Ya-Ya" by Dr. John on a trip to West Virginia for some typical college degeneracy. My friend Koss popped a tape into the stereo of the yacht-sized station wagon carrying us south. I had never heard anything like it, this sound that echoed out of the speakers as if transmitted from the darkest shadows of the most remote swamp of that alien territory of Louisiana.

I was in the backseat attempting to nail my hands to the carpet. We had stopped at some highway truck stop and purchased a bottle of ephedrine. Lacking any sense of mortality or reasonable respect for our organs, we popped 10 pills, as a start.

The inner earthquake began as a gentle massage before the first tremors took hold.

"Maybe I should ride on the roof," I said. "My eyes are blenders."

"No," Koss said, popping Dr. John into the stereo. "Listen to this."

The eerie breeze of the sirens' chorus, the back and forth with their croaking hoodoo priest, coated in a 1920 phonographic static, blew from out of the speakers and washed me out of that wood-paneled tank into the deep southern moss.

"What the hell is this?"

"Dr. John," Koss said.

Fuck.

Goddamn.

I'm sold.

And from that moment I was obsessed with New Orleans. I wanted to be in that place that inspired that unearthly song. It wasn't American. It wasn't European or African or Hispanic. It was something else. It represented the dark unknown and I wanted in.

So a few months later I booked a ticket on Amtrak and arrived in New Orleans. And that was all it took.

"This is where I want to be buried," I said to myself or my friends or whatever drunk or bartender or sorority girl I happened to be harassing at the moment.

We stayed for a week and did the things dumb fucking college kids do in New Orleans. One night I abandoned my friends and walked to Spanish Plaza where I met an old home-less black man. We sat next to the fountain and shared a beer. He told me his tragic life story and I told him I ran away from home and was now living on the streets, a real life street urchin, a gutterpunk in the making.

And then a cop shined a light in our eyes and told us to beat it.

I ran into my homeless friend once more, by chance, while my friends and I were sitting in the train station, waiting for our ride back home, to our fancy northeastern university. I saw him spot me from across the crowded lobby.

"Oh shit."

I pushed my bag full of clothes and other evidence that proved I was not a street urchin, that in fact I was a liar, under the bench.

"How are you?" he asked.

"I'm ok," I said. "I'm going home."

"So you made peace with your parents?" he asked with sincere concern.

"Yeah," I said. "I made peace. I'm going home."

He smiled and shook my hand. "I'm real happy for you. I'm glad you're getting your life back together. Good luck."

"You too," I said.

The last time I saw him he was begging money off of a Midwestern-looking couple that waved him off with unison disgust. And to this day, I don't know what was going through his mind when he spotted me with my friends and our bags waiting for the train. The night we met I fit the image of the street kid with my bleary eyes and slurred speech and unwashed jeans and dirty t-shirt. But in that train station, I was wearing the typical college-kid uniform and there could be no mistaking my lies.

But he didn't let on that he knew. All he expressed was kindness and care for my well-being.

I felt like an asshole because I was an asshole. I didn't give a shit about anything or anyone in those selfish, brain-damaging days. Everything was a kick, a fucking joke on the world and I was always ready to be the first to pull the chord.

He gave me my first taste of regret and I carry it to this day.

And now I wonder if he was one of the unlucky ones, the 2,000 who disappeared under the funhouse mirror reflections of the storm-waters.

Shit.

The reason I went off on this ancient tangent was to say that during that first trip I met my friend Quintin. He took care of us, we three drunks. He befriended us and showed us around town, taking us to the anti-tourist locales known only to locals. He fed us shots and pills and music and kindness. And after we left we kept in touch and in the ensuing years he gave me shelter whenever I returned to New Orleans, which I did nearly every year after that first.

To me, he was New Orleans. And I loved him for it.

Four years after that first trip I moved to New Orleans for good. And that same year, 1998, I experienced my first hurricane, the near-miss that was Hurricane Georges. He gave us a taste of what was to come seven years later. You'd think it would be seven years wiser but that's a claim I'm not willing to commit to paper.

I heard the hurricane reports and was none too concerned. My girlfriend was in Texas visiting her parents so I was by myself in our house on General Pershing just a few blocks off of Claiborne Avenue. I ran to the store for supplies—two cases of Budweiser and a couple packs of smokes. When I got home I ordered two large cheese pizzas from Domino's. That should do it, I figured.

The delivery man was an old white guy, a New Orleans lifer. I asked him what he thought about Georges.

"How bad do you think it's going to be?"

"Aww man, this won't be nothin'. I lived through Betsy and she was hell. But this one, it ain't gonna be shit."

An hour later I called Quintin.

"So you sticking around for the fun?"

"Hell no," he said. "I'm getting the hell out of here. This could get bad. This could be the one."

"What? The pizza delivery guy just told me not to worry about it."

"Who? Listen man, I'm getting out of here, driving to my parents' place in Lake Charles. You're welcome to come with me."

"I can't. Amanda left me with her two dogs and three cats. I can't leave them here and I sure as shit can't take them with you. Do you really think it's going to be bad?"

"I don't know man but I ain't taking any chances. But if you're going to stay do you mind checking on my place after the storm hits? I'll drop off my keys on my way out of town."

"Umm, sure. I guess."

Two hours later Quintin knocked on my front door.

"Here are the keys. Just make sure everything is ok, that none of the windows were blown out or anything. And here are a couple of brownies I made. Whatever you do don't eat them all at once. Just eat segments. They're incredibly strong. I'll give you a call later to check in."

And then he was gone, leaving me with two cases of beer, two pizzas, two dogs, three cats, the keys to his house and two incredibly potent pot brownies.

I sat at a bar we had built in what most people would call the dining room. The bar was massive and occupied a third of the room with the other two-thirds empty except for a homemade scarecrow sitting in a wheelchair. I ate a slice of pizza and opened my first beer. I turned on the news for a few minutes but it bored me so I flipped the channel. Eventually, I stuck my head out the back door to check for signs of my impending doom. All's quiet.

146

Pizza Man one, Quintin zero.

Fuck it. I unwrapped a brownie and ate half. I waited 20 minutes for the weed to do its thing, but save for a slight tingling sensation my brain remained interconnected with reality. And that wasn't what I was after. Quintin underestimated my tolerance. An hour later both brownies were consumed along with eight beers and three slices of pizza.

Time to check back in with the news. The screen was filled with a large white mass headed towards the Gulf Coast. And then came the images of thousands of people piling into the Superdome. This was slightly unnerving.

The phone rang. My friend Dave wanted to make sure I was ok. He said he was staying at a friend's place, a third floor apartment.

"You should come over," he said.

"I can't. I have to watch over the dogs and cats."

"Well, if your house is still standing after the storm can I move in? I'm getting evicted."

"Sure, that shouldn't be a problem. Wait, what do you mean, 'If your house is still standing?'"

"I don't know man. It looks bad."

An hour later the wind picked up and the rain pounded the siding. My neighbors were nailing boards over their windows. I was glued to the television, staring at Weather Lady Margaret Moore, this gigantic, red-headed Amazon. She was eating a kitten, mumbling between bites about the "end times."

"I found this little tyke hiding under my house," she gurgled, trails of blood-drool running down her lavender blouse. "There was a whole litter of them. I bagged them up and brought them to the station. They're rich in protein and the soft fur tickles your nose as you feast on their neck. To my fellow New Orleanians, this may be our only shot at survival. So I suggest you get a flashlight and look under your house for stray kittens before it's too late. By morning the streets will be overrun with cannibals, mutated people with gills and translucent skin that will allow them to thrive in the new Atlantis."

Stupid fucking Quintin and his crack-cocaine brownies. Why didn't he warn me about the side effects? He knew I had no self-control, right? Oh Jesus, the dogs are staring at me. They know what I've been thinking, about them and the cats, the thoughts that Margaret Moore has put in my head. I can't see! I've gone blind! Wait. It's just the electricity. It's gone out. Ok. Calm down. I have no electricity. Oh fuck. I have no electricity. It's Georges. He's coming. And all I got are two pizzas minus three slices and a case and a half of beer. I'm fucked. Everyone wants me to die. That's why Amanda took off, why Quintin drugged me, why Dave called to mock me from his castle tower.

I spent the night huddled on the floor of our pseudo-dining room clutching a battery-powered radio, consuming as much beer as I could to ease the effects of the brownies. The phone rang several times but I refused to answer it. I didn't want to give whoever it was, the people safely out of the way of impending brunt trauma by way of 120 m.p.h. winds, the pleasure of hearing the fear in my voice, the effects of their organized attack on my sanity.

But I'll show them. Upon their return to their former home, now a dank, watery landscape, I'll be lying in wait, my gills pulsating, the sunlight passing through my blown-glass skin, my teeth filed to points, and my appetite waiting to be quenched.

When I woke up the next morning there were no cannibals or pestilence or gilled super-humans. There was the sun and the trees and my neighbors on their porches enjoying another day in New Orleans. The storm veered to the right and we escaped the wrath of Georges. Another near-miss. I told myself I would never be fooled again by meteorologists or nature.

After being trapped in the insane asylum that was my hurricane-house for the past 18 hours I needed an escape so I pedaled my bike down Napoleon Avenue to the Club, the only Uptown bar with electricity. It was packed like Mardi Gras with the survivors of Georges looking to get wild. The city was ours. Tens of thousands had evacuated and the thousands who sought refuge in the Superdome were prisoners, barred from going home for a full day by the Morial administration. "It's too dangerous," they said. "Calm down. We know better. Enjoy the Astroturf and be thankful to be alive. We done you dirty masses good."

But the dirty masses were not happy. The storm didn't hit New Orleans. There was no damage except for some broken tree branches and busted windows. But while everyone else in New Orleans was free to go about their lives, for some insane reason the Superdome people were denied access to the exits. This was to be their home for the foreseeable future.

"Don't worry folks, you won't have to go through this again. Just have patience."

Inside the Club, we glanced at the televisions, shaking our heads at the plight of the Dome people. But what was a day, right? They'd be out soon enough. So we went about our business. The sun fell and drinks were consumed and memories erased. When I emerged 12 hours later it was morning, another day, the sun reset in the sky, herself never concerned about Georges or New Orleans or any of us.

Time to go home.

I pedaled down Napoleon Avenue doing my drunken best to maintain balance and a natural upright position while swerving through the timber-maze of branches that blanketed the street. I made it a good block and a half when a sisterhood of twigs launched an attack on the spokes of my ride and undermined both my concentration and equilibrium.

When I regained consciousness, I found myself lying in the middle of Napoleon Avenue, trapped underneath my bike as a slow crawl of cars rubbernecked past my personal disaster. I struggled to lift the metal contraption off my chest but it was no use. I was too weak, too drunk, an upturned human cockroach, or turtle. Yes, better a turtle.

I tried to right myself, but what did it matter? Chances are, if I got up I was only going to fall down again, so why not enjoy the view for a bit, for just a few minutes? The blue sky and sun and slow-drifting clouds and the breeze on my skin, the voices of passers-by encouraging me towards victory.

"You can do it upturned Turtle Man!"

And the others.

"You fucking human cockroach! Get the hell out of the street before we squish you!"

"I am not who you think I am!" I shouted, prone under my bike in the middle of Napoleon Avenue. "I am but a reflection of what our kingmaker Georges intended! I am both the cockroach and turtle that torments and teases you in the eyes of your own dreamy nightmarish hurricanes! Leave me be and one day I will rise again and reveal to you the true face of humanity!"

And then someone threw a beer can at my head.

Ow.

Good enough.

The blood of humanity.

Seven years later we were introduced to Georges' cousin Katrina. And to her he passed the family grudge. She was a new breed and would not be denied her prize. More than five feet of water sunk my old house on General Pershing and eight months later it remains empty along with the rest of the homes on that block and in the surrounding area. Complete devastation. The storm sheared off the face of one house, revealing the interior of its second story like a dollhouse.

I sat in my car and stared at the pink house I once called home, the front lawn transformed into a miniature jungle, a red "X" spray-painted on the porch shutters, and a thick brown water stain painted around the exterior. I hoped whoever lived in it at the time of the hurricane got out before landfall. And if they didn't, I hoped they had enough sense to prepare better than I did seven years earlier.

Two cases of beer, two pizzas and two high-powered pot brownies.

Jesus.

Back during the time of Georges, it being my first hurricane, I remember everyone on the news saying something about keeping an axe in the attic. Just in case. That's fucking crazy, I said. Who the fuck keeps an axe in their attic? But at the height of my pot brownie psychosis, as I sat alone in the dark listening to the wind and the battery-powered radio, I rolled through the scenarios, picturing myself having to shove two dogs and three cats into the attic as water poured into the house, lifting couches and mattresses up on its dirty surface, rising above the sinks and counters. And without an axe, what were we going to do once we were in the attic? But the scenario sounded so outlandish, even to my THC-submerged brain, that I pushed it out of mind so I could concentrate on how best to fight off the gilled-cannibals.

Now I can't help but think back. What would have happened if Georges and Katrina switched places? If the levees collapsed while I was strapped with pot brownie floaties and a scuba tank full of Budweiser?

Simple. Two dead dogs, three dead cats and one half-mad kid destined for decades in the psych ward.

But they didn't switch places.

Two of the cats, Puck and Zoe, and one of the dogs, Aisha, died before Katrina. The lone surviving dog, Danny, and cat, Grace, died shortly thereafter. As for me, well, I continue to roam free though it may be too generous to describe myself as fully alive. Every day another chunk of my sanity is chipped away.

For nostalgia's sake, once a month, I lock myself in my house with two stuffed dogs, three stuffed cats, two cases of beer, a bag of weed (too lazy to bake brownies), and two pizzas. Around 9 p.m. I turn off all the lights and wait for the floodwaters to come knocking on my door.

"It's ok little guys," I say to my glassy-eyed pets. "We're going to be just fine. It's all going to turn out like Christmas. And tomorrow, when I open that door, you'll see. The sun will be shining and New Orleans will be whole, untouched, just as we remember it. And daddy will go out for a few beers to celebrate our good luck. Just like old times."

E...11-th Entry
April 21, 2006,

TICKING GODDAMN, GODFORSAKEN A-BOMBS OF THE UNSHAKABLE FEAR OF THE REPRISE, IN SEARCH OF RELIEF FROM SOMETHING ROTTEN IMBEDDED IN OUR MINDS, TREMBLING WITH THE URGE TO DO SOMETHING. OH LORD WE KNOW NOT WHAT. YET THERE IT LIES IN WAIT AND....... IN HATE.

Quintin recently returned to disaster-central for the weekend. He bugged out of New Orleans before the storm with his girlfriend Pandora. They now live in San Francisco. When he arrived I was in Chicago.

He wrote me an email.

"I was sad to see how little things had progressed," he wrote. "I now know I made the right decision in leaving. New Orleans is not a healthy place to live."

That's right. We ain't done shit. I got the clap when I tried to separate two dogs that got stuck together humping in an abandoned house in the Ninth Ward.

I should have left them alone, as a sick monument to what could have been.

Ohhh the love that once flowed through this city. Some say it still exists. And I'm sure it does, in the sweat and alcohol-drenched beds of the good-time kids who get a kick out of a solid, meat-pounding in the shadow of the storm.

But that's not fair. There was plenty of love during Mardi Gras. And there's love between friends struggling to maintain fragile ties to sanity. But the intensity appears to be ebbing. My friends and I have reached a strange moment in these post-Katrina months, a moment in which we long for those first two months after the storm when the love flowed thick from the Bywater to Uptown. Back then we were all so goddamn raw and shaken. Back then there was little thought about the future. We were just happy to be back, to be together.

The first familiar faces began to reappear in late September/early October. It was the time of the National Guard and curfews and duct-taped refrigerators and swarms of pregnant bugs.

We were unsteady and unsure but we were back home, something most thought would never happen.

The first place I hit when I rolled into town was the Balcony Bar and the first face I saw was Kimble's, the kind Brit who loaned me his car that last Saturday before it all went to hell.

He had a beer and a smile and that's all I needed, all any of us needed. It was beautiful and simple. No complications. The city was torn the fuck up and populated by maybe 50,000 nut jobs that chose to make an early go of it. The only businesses open were bars and a handful of restaurants and it made perfect sense.

All we were interested in was reconnecting and re-numbing our wounded souls.

It was a time to take a deep breath and a careful look around, shake the head and say, "Goddamn," in a whisper.

Goddamn.

With each day that passed another familiar face arrived. And we greeted every one, be they blood brothers or causal acquaintances as if they were all willing kidney donors.

We didn't know what lay ahead of us, what would take place in the course of the next six months. It would be wrong to say we didn't care. But we didn't spend too much time sweating the details.

It was a time to share stories and beers and gorgeous New Orleans hangovers that were quickly dispatched with the twist of an early afternoon beer cap.

In quiet moments, tears came but not as frequently as they did in the first few weeks after Katrina when it wasn't unusual to dissolve into hysterics several times a day.

We were alive.

We were home.

With friends.

And wasn't that enough?

For us it was.

For us it was everything.

The time for war would come later.

The insanity and dark-hole depression had not yet hit, though the signs were slowly emerging.

We were just a damaged collection of drunks drawn to the light because it felt safe.

And we thought we were safe.

Now, eight months after the hurricane, many of us long for those halcyon nights.

* * * * * * * * *

*After the sun sets, Magazine Street between Washington
and Louisiana avenues roars to life
By Richard A. Webster New Orleans CityBusiness Staff Writer*

October 17, 2005 -- The furniture and clothing stores are shut down. The antique shops are boarded up. Radio Shack is dark. Not even the coffee shops — Rue de la Course, Starbucks and Puccino's — are open.

Hurricane Katrina has reduced the once thriving Magazine Street to block after block of broken signs and spray-painted plywood.

But when the sun sets, the stretch of Magazine Street between Washington and Louisiana avenues roars to life. Crowds teem the sidewalks outside of Sake Café and Table One waiting up to two hours for a seat. Returning locals toast each other over beer and salted margaritas at the tables outside of the Bulldog and Nacho Mama's. Friends reunite at the Balcony Bar Café and the Rendezvous to trade war stories.

Joey Ledet, general manager of Sake Café, said many of these people have been through hell, their homes destroyed, jobs lost and friends scattered across the country. By opening his sushi restaurant he provides a refuge from the madness and a semblance of normalcy. Business has never been better, he said.

"We're like Friday and Saturday night every night and that's really hard because usually we have double the staff," Ledet said. "We've had to turn away at least 100 people each night but you want to get open as soon as you can to let everyone know you're strong and resilient and that you want to be a forerunner in rebuilding the community."

The sentiment is echoed by the business owners who reopened along Magazine Street. Shane Finkelstein, owner of Nacho Mama's Mexican Grill, said he reopened out of a sense of responsibility to the city though the decision was not an easy one to make. Finkelstein lost his $200,000 house during the hurricane and will have to spend more than $10,000 to repair the damage done to his restaurant by the storm and looters who took his liquor and cash register while coating his office with raw meat.

He is trying to resurrect his business without his wife, Courtney, who will live in Atlanta with their two children, Drew, 2, and Remy, 6 months, until the city is safe for children.

"A business owner whose house is fine has nothing to lose if they reopen," Finkelstein said. "But for me, I have life-altering decisions to make. Should I buy a house, rent a house, leave my family in Atlanta or give up? When I first got back I was going to leave town for good but my friend I'm staying with was so optimistic and so was everybody we met, asking me to please reopen. It's encouraging to hear everybody want to rebuild."

Across the street at the Rendezvous, owner Steve Peterson said for him there was only one choice — return and reopen.

Even when he took his first look inside the bar and saw an ATM and poker machine missing, a flat-screen television ripped off the wall and so much booze stolen that not even 16 liquor deliveries has replenished the loss, he still said there was only one choice.

"It's not that I didn't have other options," Peterson said. "I could have stayed at the beach at St. Augustine in Florida. It was beautiful and there was opportunity. But it wasn't home. I worked too long and hard for this. I didn't think about whether we would be busy or dead, my only thought was to reopen and we would deal with whatever happened. The hurricane didn't beat us and neither did the looters."

Since reopening two weeks ago, Peterson said business has picked up right where it left off before Hurricane Katrina.

Table One can't make the same comparison because it did not exist prior to Hurricane

Katrina.

One week before the storm made landfall, Tarek Tay and Gabriel Saliba, co-owners of Byblos, a Greek restaurant with locations on Magazine Street and in Metairie, purchased the former site of The Living Room, a steak and lobster restaurant on the corner of Magazine Street and Washington Avenue.

General Manager James Mathes said it's been packed ever since the official grand opening Oct. 1.

Like Sake Café, Table One offers a full menu with sandwiches, barbecued ribs, filet mignon, salads and appetizers.

"We've seen guests who have been here every day since we opened and people who come in for lunch and dinner," Mathes said. "We're getting a pretty loyal following. It's been a blessing in disguise because, instead of having to slowly build a clientele, we've been inundated. People want to escape and not worry about going back to a construction site or a smelly house."

Unlike Nacho Mama's, Sake Café and the Rendezvous, all operating with bare-bone staffs sometimes working 12-hour shifts, Table One has a full staff, mostly from Byblos locations that aren't expected to open for weeks.

And Table One escaped the scourge of looters.

"It wasn't looted, but it was like a few people came in (after the storm), had some cocktails and a little party and hung out at the bar, which was alright by us," Mathes said

While business has been strong, it has not always been smooth.

"Some of our guests have been really rude, cutting people in line who have been waiting for hours," Ledet said. "It's tough because you wouldn't think at a time like this people would act that way but all the bars and restaurants up Magazine have been having the same problems. There are people who haven't been affected or have way too much money to be affected by anything ... but we treat everyone the same. I've even told cops that they had to wait and they walked out all mean and mad. We're operating the best we can and for those that appreciate it we appreciate them and for those who don't we hope eventually they do."

Ledet estimates 40 percent of the city's restaurants will never be seen again.

"I think a lot of restaurants won't come back and that's because they were living paycheck to paycheck and behind on bills. The businesses that weren't run right won't reopen. It's the strong businesses that will return. And if you don't open now you're not going to open because you'll lose the energy of the city reopening."

* * * * * * * * * *

Eight months later, nothing is simple.

The "illusion of safety" lies in an abandoned building, another casualty of the storm, gasping for life as blood pours out of four well-placed bullet wounds in the chest.

Our greetings have shifted from, "Man, it's fucking great to see you," to, "Are you ok? Are you sure?"

From, "Did you see Marky? He just got back into town." To, "Did you hear about Marky? He shot himself in the head."

The mean psychic residue of the storm has spread and is damn near close to blanketing the city.

That pure joy of reconnecting has given way to the deadening impact of post-Katrina life. And the things that gave us comfort in those first two months no longer do the trick. We've taken a breath and opened our eyes and accepted that nothing is going to change, that this is the world we live in. And it is fucked.

But to say that nothing has changed is not true.

Crime has returned. The old ways are making a comeback. And many are unearthing old plans, carefully crafted in early 2005, to get the hell out of New Orleans.

So not only are we living in a city 80 percent of which is blacked-out and in ruins, we are living in a devastated city that is quickly slipping back to its old corrupt ways.

So as sick as it may sound to outsiders, we gather around half empty beers and long for the months immediately after the storm. We long for the kindness and care freely offered to friends and strangers alike.

"Nothing has changed."

Quintin was right.

Not a goddamn thing has changed and it's a disheartening and damaging realization.

All the shit you think might have been purged by Katrina, well, it's back. And it sucks.

But just when you find yourself sinking into some pit of self-sorrow, you take a sick day on a Friday and drive down to the lower Ninth Ward because you haven't been there in two months. You go because you want to remind yourself of the scale of tragedy that took place, the hell unleashed.

You jump in your truck with a camera and drive down Rampart past the fully function-ing French Quarter. And as you hit St. Claude Avenue and dig in deeper the signs of life you've grown accustomed to in Uptown--open businesses, intact houses, life--are left in the rearview mirror, replaced by the heavy presence of ghosts wailing in the attics of boarded-up homes spray-painted by the National Guard.

And when you hit the lower Ninth the only difference you detect from your visit two months ago is the demolition of maybe 20 houses that once rested in the middle of the street.

The rest of it--the upturned cars and burned baby dolls, the front stoop to nowhere, the half eaten homes and brown bushes frozen in wind-torn shapes--it's all there, the charred Vietnamese girl running in the middle of the street, naked, screaming, for all to see but not many give a shit. And then you notice that the road ahead is blocked by squad cars so you maneuver your truck in an adjacent road to turn around. That's when you see the dog. Not a lost dog or emaciated dog howling for its owner, but a well-trained dog sniffing through the rubble as its trainer watches with a careful eye.

Bodies.

There are still bodies in the rubble.

Eight months later, dogs are sniffing for death.

Someone's father or mother or grandmother or grandfather.

Or baby.

The ones who didn't make it, buried so deep in the wreckage that the first sweeps missed their horror-stricken forms.

Don't look now mister but I think I see an arm.

It's not all grim all the time. We manage moments of joy and embrace holidays with a lonely ferocity. It is New Orleans after all and our ability to push our problems into the dark corners with barrels of booze has become a useful ritual.

On St. Patrick's Day we packed Magazine Street and ruptured our brains.

Take my friend Hank. One minute he's inside the Balcony and the next he's being thrown out the front door by three bartenders.

I'm standing next to him one minute and the next he's rolling around in the gutter, right in front of one of the bartenders who kicked him out, laughing and spitting beer in the air like a fountain.

One minute I'm trying to soothe the bartender's rising anger and the next I'm looking across the street at Hank, standing with his pants around his ankles, masturbating, in broad daylight, to the horror of surrounding families, pointing his crooked penis and laughing at the bartender who I'm telling, "Hey man, just let it go. He's drunk but he won't bother you anymore."

"You mean that the guy over there with his dick in his hands cackling like a fucking asshole?"

"Where? There? Well, yeah, I suppose that's him. Yeah, that doesn't look good. Shit. Ummm, well...fuck."

We tried to move Hank out of the area before the cops came but it was too late. They had him in cuffs and when I approached to ask where he was being taken to, one of the power-mad officers screamed at me in a hail of spit, "You come one fucking step closer and you'll be going to jail along with this asshole!"

So you see, we're still capable of letting it all roll down hill. We get our kicks.

* * * * * * * * *

Jeremy Justice, the master tattooist at Eye Candy who painted a $400 piece on my shoulder several weeks ago is a strong proponent of tinted windows.

Unlike Run DMC who proclaimed, "Tinted windows don't mean nothing they know who's inside," Jeremy believes in the exact opposite.

"I tint all my windows. You have to in New Orleans. No one fucks with you if you have tinted windows because they think you're a fucking drug dealer. When I evacuated for the storm I was driving through Texas and a cop pulled me over, looked at my tinted windows and said, 'You got to be kidding.' Tinted windows were illegal wherever that was and he was going to fine me but I explained the situation. I told him it was the only way to be safe in New Orleans. I said, 'You've seen what's going on in New Orleans now with the looting and raping.' And he let me go. He saw what was happening and knew what a fucked-up, dangerous city this is."

The prevailing wisdom now is that should another hurricane hit, and looters attempt to do what looters do, it will be a fucking bloodbath because the percentage of armed citizens has risen exponentially. Last time the looters took people off-guard. Next time, the streets will be lined with shell casings and bodies.

Hurricane season starts June 1 but won't really kick into high gear until August.

Before Katrina we operated under the impression that we would always avoid the big hit. Now, we're expecting to get hit again, as if it is inevitable.

There are thousands of people in FEMA trailers who will have to evacuate in the event of a hurricane as small as a Category 1. Christ, our levees are still fucked-up and the Army Corps is struggling to rebuild them to Category 3 protection by July.

But what's a poor boy to do?

Load up on ammo, tease the dog with a cat tied from a high tree branch to get the bloodlust boiling and wait for the action.

It's time to move the yardstick to where the chalk stick hits the pavement and make with the body outline.

Do you see now?

Can you see just how fractured the New Orleans mind has become in this wretched wake we've been floating in lo these many months?

Drunks and swimming trunks and bloody chunks of anger, in a crouching defensive posture, in the last desperate throes of something to be ashamed of and something to be afraid of.

Ticking goddamn, godforsaken A-bombs of the unshakable fear of the reprise, in search of relief from something rotten embedded in our minds, trembling with the urge to do something.

158

Oh lord we know not what.
Yet there it lies
In wait and
In hate.

I say "we" a lot.
But maybe it's just me.

Stop children, what's that sound?
The squishy squish of a back alley rape.
Claws on walls.
I spent all my money on whoop-dee-doo.

I used to spend much of my time railing against the feds and the incompetence of Bush.
I miss those long-gone days, when I believed in hope, when I thought help was coming
down the pike, mixed up in my belief that this wasn't the City that Care Forgot.
But it is.
So I suppose it's correct to say that little has changed, except for my transition from madman crusader to rooftop rifle crooner with a serenade in his heart and an extra clip tucked
behind his ear.
Billions in federal aid have been waved in our direction but for many it's too late. Unfor-
tunately, despite the images of the dead and dying blasted across the globe, Bush and his
pocket-whores never got the urgency of it all. How long can you leave a dying man in the
incinerator-sun, wrapped in gasoline promises before he comes to grips with his festering
mortality?
I think it's like two days.
We're going on eight months.
Yeah, it may seem like I complain a lot and whine and moan and bitch and scream and
beg.
Yeah, it may seem like I ain't got nothin' good to say.
Nothin' happy to report.
Nothin' worthy of a prayer.
Sorry Mom but I'm a drunk.
Send money Mom 'cause I'm a drunk.
Just another liberal member of the elite media who refuses to report all the good shit go-
ing on.
Ok.
The good shit.
Here goes...My friend Len got laid last night for the first time after busting up with his
girlfriend.

I know it ain't like rebuilding Charity Hospital but it's something, right?

It's the little things.

Not like coming out with a comprehensive rebuilding plan or shaming crooked politicians into autoerotic asphyxiation-induced suicide. But it's good news nonetheless.

It's got a certain sense of redemption and that's all any of us are after.

Rebound sex.

Simple.

Uncomplicated.

A new beginning.

Hope.

Momentary bliss.

We're an entire city in search of rebound sex.

May 2006,

An Appetite
to Set
Things

Riot!

SALLY? MARK? **LISTEN UP!** WHEN YOU GO TO BED TONIGHT, UNDERNEATH YOUR PILLOWS, YOU WILL EACH FIND A **BERETTA**. THAT IS THE ONLY ANSWER TO THE DARK DAYS WE FIND OURSELVES IN. FUCK VOTING. THE ONLY LEVER YOU NEED TO PULL IS THE BENT PIECE OF METAL ATTACHED TO THAT CYLINDRICAL MOUTH OF GOD.

DO YOU SEE WHAT I'M GETTING AT?

NO? YOU WILL YOU LITTLE LEACHES. AND IF IT ALL GOES WRONG, DON'T HESITATE TO OPEN FIRE ON EACH OTHER.

There are times I feel as if I've come to terms with this debris-ridden reality thrust upon my home by that motherfuckin' storm and the fantastic incompetence of the federal government.

There are times I feel as if this was how it was supposed to be.

Our bones have been exposed and at first glance we recoiled in self-conscious horror. But after a few months walking around with our femurs exposed we got a feel for the wind on our marrow.

I've gone through all the predictable stages of grief and I suppose I've landed on acceptance. Truth be told, I've only touched on three stages--grief, boiling rage and now, acceptance.

Maybe four if you count persistent, drooling drunkenness.

But this stage of acceptance has spun me backwards towards a more pure form of rage. All the problems and daily annoyances I thought had been purged by the storm have returned and nothing has pissed me off more. Not the wretched indifference of whorish politicians from Utah or Texas or the pointed insults that flow from greedy and complacent U.S. citizens who condemn us for invoking the country's moral responsibility to come to the aid of its devastated own.

"Don't give a goddamn dime to those sewer beasts!" screams Daddy Yankee at the mahogany dinner table in his two-story suburban home in lawn-care Americana. He would rather see his hard-earned tax dollars go towards a sensual Thai massage for his Droopy Dawg white senator elected by the virtue of his promise to impale Mexican heads on spikes and plant them along the border to scare off the caramel people.

After dinner's religious invocation, the dutiful and educational discussion of the day's events commences.

"Hey honey, can you please pass the gravy?" Daddy Yankee asks his salt of the earth wife.

"Of course my dear. Oh, by the way, did you hear about all that awfulness that happened in New Orleans?" Momma Salt inquires.

"You mean about all the darkies drowning in their own refuse?"

"Yes. There's talk in Congress that billions will be needed to rebuild New Orleans. What are your thoughts about that darling? Should we organize a can drive?"

Daddy Yankee prepares his children for the evening sermon.

"Sally, Mark, I want you to listen to what I'm about to say because these are lessons that will shape your adult lives. In the next few weeks you will hear a lot of talk about our moral responsibility to rebuild New Orleans. Your dope-happy professors will chant some bullshit about our supposed obligation to open up our wallets to feed the coffers of people too stupid to evacuate with a monster hurricane in their backyard and people dumb enough to live in a city 10 feet below water. When this happens I want you to look your pedophiliac teachers in their pock-marked faces and say, 'Mr. Hippie, my daddy said that he works hard for his salary and he'll be damned if his taxes go towards justifying the existence of the mentally crippled and morally depraved. My daddy said that his tax dollars would be better spent fighting terrorism and kicking the asses of welfare queens.' You see what I'm saying? Mark? I swear to God if you go gay on me I'll cut off your balls!"

"Honey!" Momma Salt gasps. "Mark isn't gay. I saw him peeking in on me while I was in the shower yesterday. Isn't that right Mark?"

"Really? Mark? Is that true? Good boy. She's a fine piece of ass, ain't she? Anyway, if your teachers try to even talk about New Orleans you stand up, pull out your peter, urinate on their sandals and walk right out of class. And I'll betcha your classmates will follow."

Oh my!

Little Sally and Mark done gone down the rabbit hole.

Done gone down the possum pit.

Be careful.

Watch your heads kids.

If you choose to resurface with

These new beliefs in tow,

Prepare to familiarize yourself with

The taste of the shovel and shit.

But the time for battling those on the outside, trying to cleanse their eyes and make them see the truth, has come to an end. They've made their positions clear. They have proven to be immune to logic and debased verbal obscenities, so I find myself forced to deal with the enemies within.

Yeah, and that takes me back to my original point, the return to those awful, tedious pre-storm New Orleans days.

The sorrow and communal grief of Katrina has morphed into an awful, blind passion to return to those days of yore that have miraculously been re-imagined as the Golden Years. And so I find myself, ruined liver and all, as an agent of reason wailing in the face of a legion of fools wearing, "God Love July 2005," t-shirts.

What most have forgotten is that pre-Katrina New Orleans was already a devastated city.

Instead of unmoored houses scattered in the middle of battered streets, there were bodies and nihilistic young men delivering 2,000 m.p.h. blasts of wind in the form of bullets. Tiny hurricanes every damn day and night.

This was a city drowning under a slow flood of ignorance, corruption, cynicism, racism, poverty, and crime for decades. The cries that rained out from those tropical attics on August 30, 2005 as the floodwaters rose were nothing new. The people of New Orleans have been wailing into the uncaring night for decades. But unlike that fateful week when the National Guard, Red Cross, and good Samaritans from across the country came rushing to their rescue, their pre-Katrina pleas for mercy that echoed through generations went unheeded.

Fuck it y'all.

That's capitalism.

A necessary evil.

You expect everyone to be able to afford an SUV?

Should everyone be so lucky to attend $15,000 per-year private high schools?

Some kids are born wealthy, others not so much.

That's just the way it goes man.

Without the poor and unfortunate we wouldn't have the chance to be charitable.

Without the fucked-up and lost we wouldn't know what to do with the spare change jingling and jangling in our pockets.

Here man, here's a quarter.

Ahhh, that felt good. I should reward myself with a watch or some fake tits.

Maybe a third testicle to wow the whores.

So cry on noble souls.

You gotta buy your catastrophe

You gotta pay for salvation

You gotta burn to be cured.

I'm a tired, broken record.

Eighty percent of New Orleans underwater.

Eighty percent of New Orleans devastated.

More than 300,000 people displaced. And that doesn't even take into account the people of St. Bernard or Plaquemines parishes.

Crime on the rise.

Small businesses dying.

Our people are slowly going insane, chasing after sister suicide.

Does it ring a bell?

But there is good news.

Mardi Gras and Jazz Fest were successful, holy experiences.

The city has proven itself capable of hosting major conventions. Restaurants and hotels throughout the habitable strip of land, from Uptown through the French Quarter, are for the most part back on-line.

The curbside refrigerators are gone along with the swarm of insects.

And yesterday a traffic light on Claiborne Avenue flickered to life, if just for a second.

So if you run into one of our displaced people in your hometown, tell them about it. Tell them all about the good news.

But when you're talking with friends, tell them about everything else.

Tell them about the acres of nothingness.

And in the quiet moments, utter five simple, one-syllable words: The dead we owe you.

The city is moving on in epileptic fits. Hurricane season approaches and our levees remain a patchwork of lazy intentions. Large pockets of people are packing their bags and fleeing, self-imposed excommunication on the eve of the Second Coming. They tried to make a go of it, but when the evening news unveiled their newest graphic, "Countdown to Hurricane Season," it proved to be too much to take.

No more God, please, no more.

There is palpable terror in some circles.

For the rest, it's inevitability.

Or fuck all.

I got an appetite to set things riot.

But first we got a mayor to elect. Landrieu or Nagin. A toss-up.

In national elections social issues such as abortion and gay marriage and patriotism and dirty tricks cloud the issues. But here in New Orleans, we have something pure in terms of the vote. No sideshows. No wedge issues.

Typically people vote and watch the results and get angry or happy or nothing at all. It happens and it's over and people move on. But not this election.

The decisions we make will shape this city and touch future generations until the next hurricane makes awful love to our shores.

We are voting for something people will be able to touch decades from now. If we get it right, we will be remembered as the Ones who saved New Orleans, who put aside those pre-Katrina days, the old dead-on-arrival ways that doomed us to a perpetual third world existence.

We will be remembered as the saviors of New Orleans.

But if we get it wrong, if we allow the status quo to carry on and choke progress, if we fail to riot on the thrones of the sick politicians who drove this holy city into the ground, then we will be cursed by priests and the poor and the bleeding dead.

Wild packs of children drooling over rat bones in the same flooded-out homes that litter our present-day landscape will bear the scars of our failures.

We will be responsible.

And we will be punished accordingly.

Daddy Yankee slams a fist on the dining table and screams for Momma Salt to wrap him in the flag.

"Sally, Mark, do you see what I am wearing?" Daddy Yankee says, tugging at his stars and stripes cloak. "This is all that matters, not some pagan fleur-de-lis favored by the mongrels in that city vomited out by the Mississippi River. Listen up! I got some wisdom I need to spill on your brains. It comes from long years of listening to talk radio. And it goes a little something like this--we're all fucked. When you go to bed tonight, underneath your pillows, you will each find a Beretta. That is the only answer to the dark days we find ourselves in. Last week I adopted 50 abandoned cats and dogs. Tomorrow, after church, I'll set the beasts free in the backyard and we'll practice your aim. This, my children, is the key to your survival and the survival of not only our city but this country. Fuck voting. The only lever you need to pull is the bent piece of metal attached to that cylindrical mouth of God. Oh weary be the soul that embodies the truth! That's from the Good Book. We are besieged from all sides by deceivers and sinners. What happened in New Orleans, it happened because all them wretched beasts of addiction down there denied America and God. They didn't listen to their daddies! The liberal Satanists on CNN are saying that the government and Bush caused the flood. Bullshit! I don't believe in nature, but if I did, I'd say nature was trying to cull from its population a cancer. We don't owe those fuckers anything. The people of New Orleans have been targeted for extermination. We need to wall off that city, let pestilence and their murderous and self-abusive ways run their course. And if in 10 years when we reenter that harem of iniquity and find that somehow they survived and reproduced, we will gun them down, incinerate their fingerprints and detonate strategically placed bombs forever sinking that voodoo realm into the dark mud of its unnatural origins. This is the only way to preserve our kind. Do you see what I'm getting at? No? You will you little leaches. You'll see. And if it all goes wrong, don't hesitate to open fire on each other. Don't look at me like that you little ingrates! Listen to your father. And don't worry about your mother. I'll take care of her. We've got an understanding, right honey?"

"I'm sorry?" Momma Salt says. "Did you say something honey? I was distracted by this special on PBS about those poor people in New Orleans. It seems like they're really having a tough go of it. I feel like we should do something to help them out."

Daddy Yankee stands up, sheds the flag from around his shoulders, and tosses it on the back of his chair

"I was just teaching your children about right and wrong. But talk is one thing. Maybe it's time for a demonstration. Sally, be a good girl and close the curtains. I think it may be time your momma gets with the program. Mark, throw the tarp on the floor. Democracy can at times be messy. But I do believe it's time for me to cast my vote. Honey, I'm gonna need you to take off your jewelry and place it about 15 feet from where you're standing. And then I need you to return to that exact point. Precision and detail is everything. And blood splatter is chaotic. Sally? Mark? Don't be scared. This is the way of the world. People die. And sometimes they're murdered. But other times, they are sacrificed."

"Is this where you want me to stand?" Momma Salt asks. "Should I get the camera?"

"No. All I need you to do is close your eyes and do your part. We've always said that the only thing that matters is the children, right? Well, this is your chance to teach them the ultimate lesson—that weakness is a sin punishable by the ultimate price. Just close your eyes and think about all of those poor black crackheads of New Orleans, the ones who you spend so much time worrying about. Can you do that for me?"

"Of course I can dear. I pray for their souls every night."

"Good. Gooooood."

Time comes to a slow crawl in the house of Daddy Yankee as he fixes Momma Salt in the sight of his sawed-off. Poor, damaged Sally and Mark crouch behind the leather recliner covered in duct-tape where their wild-eyed poppa drinks whiskey and snaps back the pages of "Smiling Areolas" magazine before drifting off into semen and Vaseline dreams. The oven alarm buzzes and the smell of burning chocolate cake wafts through the kitchen to the dining room.

"Smells like dessert," Momma Salt says.

"No," Daddy Yankee responds. "It smells like victory."

A thunderclap rattles the support beams and the scent of smoldering hair overcomes the bowls of potpourri that decorate this pristine slice of Americana.

A heavy thud on the wooden floor.

And two tiny gasps from the corner.

Daddy Yankee rests his shotgun against the wall and sits back down at the dinner table.

"Sally? Mark? Take your seats. The mashed potatoes are getting cold. And when you're finished eating, get the lime. I'm gonna show you how to properly clean up a disaster and do it without whining like those little bitches in New Orleans. This is the spirit of America. This is true grit and resolve. This is progress. And if I catch either one of you crying, well, we're going to have another exercise in civic action. This is the difference between us and the animals. This is what makes us unique. And later tonight, if you're lucky, I'll show you the pleasure that can be derived from a rolled up copy of the Constitution. This is a great day to be Americans! So fuck New Orleans. There's no such thing as truth to power. It's all about power over truth. Now, if you'll excuse me, your father has a date with an unlit room, National Geographic and a straight razor. But I ain't talking about no death-kick. I'm just looking for insight into the mind of the enemy. Turn off the lights when you think you can handle your demons. And if you hear something shuffling in the blackness, don't be scared. It's just your beloved father, waiting for his eyes to adjust to the nothingness, so he can get a good look at your fear."

Interlude

Oh Come All Ye Crazies

Transvestite gang pesters Magazine Street

By Richard A. Webster New Orleans CityBusiness Staff Writer

June 24, 2006 -- Robyn Lewis, owner of Dark Charm fashion and accessories for women, represents the first line of defense for the Magazine Street shop owners. She is the first to see them come strutting in their pumps down St. Andrew Street, the bewigged pack of thieves who have plagued the Lower Garden District since May.

Like an SOS flare, Lewis grabs her emergency phone list and starts calling.

"They're coming," she warns Eric Ogle a salesman at Vegas, a block down Magazine Street. Ogle, who was terrorized by the brazen crew two months earlier, alerts neighboring Winky's where manager Kendra Bonga braces for the onslaught.

Soon every shop owner in the 2000 block of Magazine Street has been alerted.

Sarah Celino at Trashy Diva eyes the door, ready to flip the lock at the first sight of the ringleader's pink jumpsuit and fluorescent red wig.

Down at Turncoats, where the fashion-happy gang once made off with more than $2,000 in merchandise, store manager Wes Davis stands ready.

Davis said it wasn't supposed to be like this. They survived Hurricane Katrina's Category 3 winds and the ensuing looters. They reopened despite the long odds of doing business in a devastated city. The last thing the Magazine Street shop owners expected to threaten their survival was a crime ring of transvestites.

"They're fearless," said Ogle. "Once they see something they like they won't stop until they have it. They don't care, they'll go to jail. It's really gotten bad. You know it's ridiculous when everyone on the block knows who they are."

The transvestites first appeared in March when they raided Magazine Street like a marauding army of kleptomaniacal showgirls, said Davis, using clockwork precision and brute force to satisfy high-end boutique needs.

They first hit Vegas March 31 while Ogle was working.

"They come in groups of three or four. One tries to distract you while the others get the stuff and run out the door. It's very simple," Ogle said.

Next door at Winky's, Bonga heard people screaming inside Vegas, then saw a blur of cheap wigs and masculine legs in designer shoes streak past her door.

"All of a sudden our UPS guy dove out of the store and tried to tackle them and there's little Eric from next door on the sidewalk with a bunch of stuff he managed to grab from one of the guys," Bonga said. "The other two guys took off down the street and jumped into a car driven by a real girl."

Ogle gave police a description of the perpetrators — African-American males ranging in height from 6 feet to 6-5. They all wore the same midriff shirts and dreadlock wigs.

"They're all very skinny and very flamboyant," Ogle said.

Two hours after the police left, the transvestites returned to Magazine Street to storm Turncoats just a block away from Vegas, and made off with more than $2,000 in merchandise.

"They move like clockwork," Davis said. "Two thousand dollars is a lot for our store to lose, especially being in the slow summer season. It makes it so I can't even mark my stuff down as much as I want to because I'm trying to make up for what I lost."

In the ensuing weeks, the gang of transvestites continued their reign of terror. Sometimes they come dressed as men, though Bonga said it is obvious who they are based on their delicately plucked eyebrows. Sometimes they bring 2-year-old children to add to the level of distraction. They once returned to Vegas holding an "infant" that really was a Cabbage Patch doll wrapped in a blanket.

"They'll make themselves scarce for a few weeks and then one day you'll be busy with a customer and all of a sudden there's a whole slew of them in your store and there's nothing you can do because you're there by yourself," Lewis said.

The New Orleans Police Department investigated the Turncoats robbery but unless police catch a shoplifter in the act or in possession of stolen property there is little they can do besides take a report, said NOPD spokeswoman Bambi Hall.

"If store security states that someone took something, and then by the time we apprehend them they don't have the property, then there's really nothing we can do because it's their word against the (suspect)," Hall said.

Lewis said she understands the understaffed NOPD has bigger priorities than to "catch a drag queen running down the street with an armful of clothing." So the store owners created their own watchdog system unofficially known as the "Drag Queen Alert List," a comprehensive phone roster of every business on the block with stars next to those who carry guns.

When one shop owner spots a gang member, they immediately warn everyone on the block and raise their defenses in unison.

When they enter Turncoats, Davis said he locks them inside the store, which "freaks them out," and they leave.

Celino said she doesn't even wait for them to enter the store.

"A couple weeks ago, a group of them was outside and one looked like the guy who came in here and ripped us off so I locked the door on them," Celino said. "I know maybe that's rude, if they really were innocent people, but there's nothing else we can do. You look like the queens who ripped us off so I'm sorry but I have to lock the door."

Ogle and Bonga say they regret being forced to resort to such profiling but they feel they have no other choice. The transvestites, Ogle said, appear to be drug-addicted and fearless in their lust for designer shoes, jackets and jewelry.

"The city's not functioning the way it was and I'm sure a lot of them were getting some kind of government aid, which they probably aren't getting any more so they're incredibly desperate," Ogle said.

And sometimes violent.

When Lewis co-owned Trashy Diva, they attacked one of her partners in the French Quarter location, throwing her to the ground and tossing a heavy mannequin on top of her.

"They're kind of confused because they think they're women so they don't mind hitting women, but they're dudes. If you get hit by one it's like getting hit by a dude. ... Because the police are so poorly staffed, we're kind of on our own but the system we have seems to be working. I haven't seen them in at least a week but they'll be back. They're never gone for long."

Nagin Corn Town

13th Entry
July
2006,
Inside the
Green
Zone

I SAW A BLACK
MOTHER
SITTING
ON
THE
CURB

WITH

HER TWO
YOUNG BOYS, NEITHER OLDER THAN 10.

"MOMMA? WHAT DOES THAT MEAN?"
ONE OF THE LITTLE ONES ASKED.
MOMMA DOESN'T MOVE OR SHIFT HER TIRED EYES.

"HUSH UP. IT DON'T MEAN NOTHIN'."

I SHOULD HAVE STAYED IN CHICAGO.

I SHOULD HAVE NEVER COME BACK.

One of my best friends from high school died since I last wrote in this thing, this worthless, pointless self-indulgent testament to one man's weakness.

He died at the age of 33 and it had nothing to do with New Orleans. He lived in Chicago with a wife, two kids and a newborn. He was driving down the road when something in his heart went wrong.

And that was that.

I stood in the funeral home in a suit, shaking, unable to look directly into the open casket. There was a line of well-wishers. I took my place and waited, head down, shuffling forward, three steps, two steps, one step closer.

My friend's wife stood at the head of the line, accepting kind words and comforting sentiments.

And then, there I was, at the head of the line, staring at my friend's love. She looked at me and smiled.

"Rich. I didn't know you were here. Thank you so much for coming. Tom loved you." We held each other.

She was so strong.

With her arms around me, she whispered in my ear, "Let's go say goodbye to Tom." She took hold of my hand and led me to the casket.

Tom didn't look like Tom. Anyone who has been to an open casket funeral knows that. He looked like a crude rendering of an old friend.

Angela and I stood next to the casket, holding hands, staring down.

This was real pain. Hers, not mine.

"He knows you're here Rich," she said.

I flew up on Friday and left on Monday.

Before the storm a Confederate flag attached to a trailer-like home on the edge of the highway greeted travelers before they took the I-10 split to New Orleans. The wind would tickle and jostle its albino Southern balls creating an undulating Howdy-Do to visitors and returning locals.

"We missed you. Welcome to the city Progress forgot."

Driving back from the airport I noticed the flag was gone, most likely folded up in a militaristic-like ritual hours before the storm hit.

But I like to think that Katrina ripped it from its moorings during the height of her whipping dudgeon, flipped it high into the wind where it hovered and spun like a little racist galaxy, before it plunged back to Earth, stars and bars and all that hatred, rocketing through the trailer window, impaling the proud rednecks who hung it with peckerwood care. Or maybe it blew away on a 100 m.p.h. gust. Maybe it landed in the river or Lake Pontchartrain or maybe it fell on the roof of a Ninth Ward house where a black family had sat for days waiting to be saved.

And maybe that family grabbed hold of that relic of southern pride and waved it in the air catching the attention of a passing helicopter that descended with a ladder to salvation. Oh those mighty stars and bars!

Or maybe that family used it to wipe their asses. Either way, a fitting end.

But whatever its fate, the spirit of that flag lives on long and hard. After Nagin won reelection someone decided to spray paint a congratulatory note on the metal bases of several lampposts.

"Nagin, Boon town."

Now, New Orleans has never been known as a pillar of education but I got the point, right? A slight misspelling.

Nagin. Boom town. As in, "Nagin is going to make this place boom, pop and explode with hope and prosperity."

That's nice I thought.

He's really rallied the city behind him.

Good for Nagin.

The other day as I rolled to a stop at the intersection of St. Charles and Broadway, from a distance I spotted another one of these congratulatory messages, only this tagger managed to correctly spell the second word.

Instead of "Nagin Boon Town" or "Boom Town" it read, "Nagin Coon Town."

The original one, "Nagin Boon Town," had been altered by a Good Samaritan to conceal its racist sentiment. It was on a post across the street from Tipitina's on Tchoupitoulas. On the other side of the street was a bus stop where the black employees of Sav-A-Center often wait for up to an hour or more for their ride home, post-storm public transportation being spotty at best. So at this particular spot, someone had strategically spray-painted "Nagin Coon Town," knowing the hated, car-less African Americans would be forced to stare at it from their bus stop perches.

Let it burn in their brains.

Let it seep in so hopefully they will seep out of town.

Go to Houston where the rest of your kind was dumped.

One night I stopped at the "Boon Town" Intersection. While waiting for the traffic light to turn green I saw a black mother sitting on the curb with her two young boys, neither older than 10. It was dusk and the bus was nowhere in sight. But across the street the altered invocation to the worst in mankind sang out with terrible intent.

"Momma? What does that mean?" one of the little ones asked.

Momma doesn't move or shift her tired eyes.

"Hush up. It don't mean nothin'."

The two boys stare at the lamppost graffiti, their innocent brown eyes tracing the curves of every hard word.

Was this what the fucker wanted? Did he want to hurt children, like these two boys? Did he want to make it known to the littlest that they were nothing more than animals?

Someone behind me started to bang on his horn but I refused to move. I burned with hatred.

I should have stayed in Chicago.

I should have never come back.

It should have been me, not Tom in that casket.

A few days later I saw a black bumper sticker with white lettering stuck on a stop sign.

"David Duke for Mayor."

Time to nail tree branches to my arms and shoulders.

Time to stick twigs in my stomach and leaves in my mouth. Time to crouch low behind a bush at an intersection with lampposts and stop signs, armed with a bag of nails, a case of beer and a Jai Alai scoop. And wait.

Wait for them to come with their bumper stickers and spray paint.

I'll be the messenger and their flesh will be the medium.

* * * * * * * * *

Experts: NO race relations crumble under post-Katrina stress
By Richard A. Webster New Orleans CityBusiness Staff Writer

August 14, 2006 -- Shortly after Hurricane Katrina, a new breed of graffiti replaced the storm-related markings of search-and-rescue Xs and pleas for help that became a part of life after the hurricane.

Crude drawings of African-Americans drowning in the Ninth Ward blanketed the bathroom walls of the Avenue Pub on St. Charles Avenue. Management painted over the racist hieroglyphics only to see them return weeks later.

A few blocks away, at the intersection of Prytania and Erato streets, a bumper sticker plastered on a stop sign warned an unnamed but understood group of people to "Go back to Houston."

From Mayor C. Ray Nagin declaring his desire for a "chocolate city" to St. Tammany Parish Sheriff Jack Strain warning people with dreadlocks and "chee wee" hairstyles that they will be targeted if found wandering the streets of the North Shore, race relations in the greater New Orleans area have hit rock bottom, local experts say.

"There has been so much loss and grief in this area that tempers are short, trust is down and suspicion is up," said Mike Cowan, chairman of the New Orleans Human Relations Commission. "In any relationship when you get those conditions it's a dangerous time."

The anonymous scrawl on light posts and bathroom walls reflects the rising tide of racial bitterness and anger, said Lance Hill, executive director of the Southern Institute for Education and Research at Tulane University.

"In the first few days after Katrina I met many white people who felt Katrina was the best thing that ever happened to New Orleans," said Hill. "It destroyed the black community and in one fell swoop had eliminated crime, poverty, problems with the schools and the burden on social services.

"We've gone through a period of racial polarization and now there are a lot of people coming back to the city who are angry and feel like they were kept out because of the color of their skin or because they are poor. We know from history that when we ignore these ethnic conflicts they erupt into an even worse form."

Former New Orleans City Councilwoman Jacquelyn Brechtel Clarkson, whose district included the million-dollar homes of the French Quarter and the public housing projects in Algiers, said she has been forced to field accusations against the wealthy white population.

"It's absurd because the displaced people were not all black," Clarkson said. "My children and grandchildren were displaced and they're middle-class white. One of my two brothers and two of my nieces lost everything. I would say to both sides it's not all black and white. My greatest fear is we're going to lose our middle class, both black and white."

Despite overseeing a racially-mixed district, Clarkson said she fell victim to the anti-white backlash in her unsuccessful bid to win a council-at-large seat. According to a Louisiana Recovery Authority poll that asked respondents the importance of returning the city to its pre-Katrina racial demographics, 63 percent of African-Americans said it was extremely important compared to only 25 percent of whites.

Tanya Harris, a Ninth Ward community organizer, said during the recent city elections a group of white politicians visited the Lower Ninth Ward and suggested relocating the entire community.

"Why as a white man can you say these people need to be moved somewhere else as if we're cattle?" Harris said. "The first thing Katrina did, if there is any good aspect about the storm, is it exposed a lot of things, things we've been knowing for a long time which

have finally come to light."

There have been two stages of life in post-Katrina New Orleans — before Nagin's re-election and after, said Hill.

"Before the election, wealthy white people were ascendant in the recovery process and there was no question in my mind that in the 27 years I've been in New Orleans that the power configuration had reverted back to pre-Marc Morial days. The Uptown white elite were running the city and pretty arrogant about that, and they realized they couldn't implement their plans if the city government was controlled by African-Americans."

Nagin's re-election changed everything, Hill said.

"What happened since Nagin got elected, the mentality I've seen emerge is really pretty appalling. ... Typically these people are bitter and feel dispossessed. They feel they had won the city back from African-Americans after Katrina and then they lost it. Now they present themselves as victims and wallow in self-pity, some almost professionally."

Pastor Emmanuel Smith of the Israelite Baptist Church in Central City said much of the blame for the deterioration in race relations falls on the shoulders of the criminal element of the African-American population that is responsible for the recent surge in gangland slayings.

"It has separated people because most of the crime is being perpetrated by young black men and that alienates the people of a white nature," Smith said. *"It's a fear factor and results in, 'You stay on your side of town and I'll stay on my side of town.'"*

Hill said when people feel like their ethnicity is the source of a trauma, they emotionally numb themselves to the people who they feel are responsible.

"The way people cope with being driven out of their homes or with crime is to make themselves insensitive to their own feelings and in turn insensitive to the feelings of other people to the point where they feel they have a right to victimize that other group."

To accomplish that end, the Southern Institute recruited Ervin Staub, a professor of psychology at the University of Massachusetts, is helping to develop a model of community healing, dialogue and reconciliation that can be implemented in the communities of New Orleans.

"We have to accept the fact that we've experienced not just a natural disaster trauma but an ethnic trauma," said Hill. *"Whether you agree with people's interpretation of events we have large numbers of people black and white who feel they have been victimized because of the color of their skin."*

No matter what the current situation, Harris said it is important that people are finally addressing the issue of race in New Orleans.

"Katrina put New Orleans under the national microscope and now we have outsiders coming in questioning what actually went on in New Orleans before Katrina to foster this environment. It's uncomfortable to talk about but you can't heal a wound if you keep it covered all the time."

And from New Orleans the disease spreads outward to Jefferson Parish.

The bumper sticker plastered on the light pole at the intersection of Carrolton Avenue and Veterans Memorial Boulevard in Metairie conveyed a clear message in four simple words.

"David Duke for Mayor."

All that remains of the sticker is a rectangular outline after someone peeled it off recently, but for months it went untouched — a reminder for the thousands of people traveling down the boulevard that race relations in Orleans and Jefferson parishes remain an issue post-Katrina.

Bill Knecht, a board member of Erace, an anti-racism organization in New Orleans, said many people thought there was an opportunity after the hurricane for people of all races to come together. But not only did it never materialize, things have gotten worse, he said.

"It's not the Big Easy anymore," Knecht said. "People are distracted by fixing their houses and dealing with Road Home. All the good intentions about getting together and dealing with these issues, people don't have the time or emotional and physical energy. I see things deteriorating as evidenced by the increased hostility toward Latin-American folks as characterized by the issue of the taco trucks in Metairie."

In June, the Jefferson Parish Council changed its laws to restrict mobile food vendors, most of which serve Mexican fare, from operating in the parish.

In Marrero, at the intersection of Barataria Boulevard and the West Bank Expressway, a black-and-white sticker affixed to a metal pole, just underneath a sticker of the Confederate flag, reads, "Wake up white people!"

Mike Cowan, chairman of the New Orleans Human Relations Commission, a municipal agency tasked to enforce the city's human rights laws, said the appearance of such hate-filled bumper stickers, while disappointing, is not surprising.

"The ethnic mix of city is in dramatic flux," he said. "One example is the percentages between black and white are now more balanced and the Hispanic population is much larger. We're going to be more like a tri-racial city whereas before we were a biracial city with a few other people mixed in. I think it's bound to cause tensions temporarily. Any time the balance of power in a city shifts, it's going to be unsettling."

Lance Hill, executive director of the Southern Institute for Education and Research at Tulane University, said distrust between African-Americans and whites in New Orleans is at an all-time high.

African-Americans believe they are unwanted and that the local, state and federal governments have done everything in their power to rid the city of low-income minorities, he said. Whites, meanwhile, lay the blame for the rising murder rate and the city's inability to improve and move forward squarely on the shoulders of the African-American population.

178

"There's a profound racial distrust and resentment and hatred that has shaped the life of the city the last couple of years," Hill said. "Conventional wisdom is people who went through hell are more sensitive to others, but the fact is they aren't more sensitive. Oftentimes they are downright indifferent to the suffering of other people."

In Jefferson Parish, where large numbers of minorities have relocated post-hurricane, public displays of intolerance may be even greater, Hill said.

Though the majority of the population is interested in racial healing and learning how to live side by side with their new neighbors, he said there are significant numbers of people who saw Jefferson Parish as a refuge from African-Americans and the problems of New Orleans. These are the people having difficulty coping with the demographic change, Hill said.

"White-flight communities, which Jefferson was at one time, are conducive to a mentality that you don't have to learn to live with other people, you don't have to reconcile with other people because you can just pack up and move, which is why we're seeing a migration of people to the parishes north of the lake," Hill said.

Cowan and Hill are involved in efforts to heal growing racial tensions in the city. They have organized listening sessions for racial and ethnic groups to air their grievances with the goal of solutions being implemented in Orleans and Jefferson parishes.

The key, both said, is to get each group to understand the experiences, pain and concerns of the other.

"If you think water and wind destroyed your parents' lives, you don't spend the rest of your life being mad at water and wind because you can't get vengeance on it," Hill said. "But if you think people from another ethnic group caused harm and suffering for your parents and family, you'll likely spend the rest of your life caught up in endless fantasies of vengeance and turn that into a cycle of violence."

* * * * * * * * * *

A letter to all my friends:

Believe your nightmarish visions of New Orleans. On Sunday morning at about 4 a.m. the cops found five teenagers slaughtered in an SUV in Central City, a few blocks away from where I used to live just off Martin Luther King Jr. Boulevard. It was the culmination of a series of vicious slayings. So now, more than five months after the majority of the National Guard contingent left us, thinking all was well, they have been asked to return with their submachine guns and heavily armored trucks, to once again patrol our dying streets.

It's a massive setback for New Orleans. And to compound the problem, every day 3-alarm fires eat away at our corrupted landscape, thousands of vacant homes populated by lighter-happy crackheads, Hispanic laborers desperate for shelter and huddled masses of homeless men and women. The total number of fires hasn't increased but the size and scope have raged at an unprecedented level, fueled by a decimated fire department short on men, driving a fleet of trucks severely damaged during the storm and prone to breaking down at inopportune times.

We're living in the Rapture, a strange place to be.

So stay away from New Orleans.

Stay far away.

And in typical fashion, the right-wing attacked. Limbaugh scoffed at the return of the National Guard and said Florida never had to call in the military after a hurricane to deal with crime.

No way. They're tough in Florida, not like the animals in New Orleans.

What that rat-tailed fucker failed to consider is whether any major city in Florida had been completely destroyed by a hurricane. Of course, none of these brain-dead scumbags have stepped foot in New Orleans since Katrina so how can I expect them to give a damn about the facts or the people they're radio-lynchin'?

The mindless Headline News mannequin Nancy Grace had newly elected councilmember Stacy Head on her program and asked her, "Can you think of another city that has had to call in the National Guard to deal with their crime problem?"

Head, displaying perfect logic, responded, "Can you name another city that went through something like Katrina?"

Grace, in her most pompous and bimboish manner, spit, "I didn't ask that. Don't change the question. I asked whether any city has had to call in the National Guard to deal with crime."

What this tremendous example of inbreeding failed to realize is that you cannot ask the first question without taking into account the second.

It just goes to show that 10 months after Katrina people still don't fucking get it. They don't get that the majority of our city is still a ghost town. They don't understand the devastation and never will. And for that I have nothing but contempt for them. People who have not lived in this city for a significant period of time post-hurricane--save for those locals who bolted afterwards--don't have the right to judge us.

You can't understand what we've gone through just by reading newspapers or watching CNN. And I won't even comment on the drooling foreheads who rely on Fox News. They were doomed to a life of dementia the minute they said, "You know, Bill O'Reilly really makes a lot of sense."

So fuck them.

The National Guard should never have left us in the first place.

But they did and here we are, a city beset by lunatics and inadvertent arsonists while our elected officials lube up their ergonomic chairs for dark pleasures.

Don't look now New Orleans but a 400-foot dragon with a puritanical hatred for alcohol and an Oliver Cromwell-like sense of fair play has emerged from the Mississippi River. "Well, that's what they get for building a city next to the watery bed of a narrow-minded teetotaler dragon," said the glowingly white, fantastically patriotic, stars and bars humping commentator Sean Hannity when told of the Bible-righteous serpent. "Best we just let the giant lizard have his way with New Orleans. Why waste our precious resources trying to protect this city of sinners and ignorant brutes? This would never have happened in the heartland where true Americans live."

There's not a plague in New Orleans, but many would have you believe that we the people are the plague. So I'm trying to do you all a favor by giving you a simple piece of advice—stay away from New Orleans. Now is not the time to consort with us unless you want to be damned by association.

But, if you choose to come and help wrap our wounds, like thousands of others have, from college students to political radicals to born-again believers, you will forever be honored in our memories and words.

But for the hate-filled play-by-play announcers on talk radio and political cable shows, I suggest you heed my initial warning. You are neither welcome nor safe here in New Orleans.

At least not in my eyes, my crosshair vision.

* * * * * * * * *

Dear Mr. John Gibson of Fox News--

After reading your column regarding the return of the National Guard to New Orleans I took a few days to calm down before responding.

This is not how I normally operate but my therapist has tried to instill in me the virtue of restraint.

I sent her an early draft of this letter but she has been missing for three days. So I scrapped the original and decided to speak from the heart.

So understand that though my words may be offensive they come from a place of true hatred. Here goes…..

Do you do any research before you shit out these mind-rambling testaments to your punch-dumb brain?

Before you answer that, let me ask you a simple question--have you been to New Orleans since Katrina?

Here's another, you head-bloated moose-fucker--have you witnessed the devastation? Do you know that 80 percent of New Orleans remains a ghost town?

Or do you just dismiss us as a city of ignorant Democrats as the other right wing talk-vomit babies do?

I'll wait a few seconds to give you a chance to clear your throat of Georgie-boy's presidential pubic hair.

All better?

Ok, let's get started.

First, you said the NOPD is up to pre-Katrina staffing levels. False. The NOPD is roughly 200 officers down from where it was and if you speak to the cops on the street, as opposed to the spokespeople or superintendent, they will tell you that the numbers are even lower than reported.

Second, even before Katrina the department said it was short 400 officers of what was needed to effectively patrol the city. So in reality we are down 600 men.

So that's the first part of your rant shot to hell.

Next, you choose to hail former LAPD chief Daryl Gates as some sort of heroic, macho savior whose spirit we should follow to cure all of our inner-city woes. It don't fucking matter that the guy oversaw one of the most corrupt police forces in modern times. Nope. That don't mean shit to you.

All that matters is that there is an iron fist in charge to keep the animals in line. And we all know who you consider the animals to be, don't we?

But I suppose lionizing a rat like Gates falls in line with Fox News' love for disgraced public figures such as Oliver North, Mark Fuhrman, Bernard Kerik, Curtis Sliwa, Tom Delay and Newt Gingrich.

It's not the sin that matters, so long as the sinner hates liberals, Democrats and African Americans.

"Imagine Daryl Gates and his LAPD during the riots in '92 calling in the National Guard to go get Damian "Football" Williams in his South Central crib after he was caught on tape bashing Reginald Denny's head in," you wrote. "No way. Gates went and did it himself with a phalanx of LAPD cars and cops. Ray Nagin needs to employ the same approach as Gates."

You posture yourself as a journalist and yet you seem blind to the facts on the ground.

Let me put it as simply as possible so even you can understand.

And to be honest, it makes me sad I even have to explain this to you, that you were dumb enough not to get it on your own.

But you're not dumb, are you? You are simply a partisan hack willing to slander an entire city to prop up your lonely hatred.

Ok. Listen up.

The South Central riots were a single moment of unrest that had no impact on the size of the LAPD. The riots did not wipe out a majority of the homes of the LAPD and they did not destroy half of the LAPD stations or its squad cars. And the riots only impacted a small section of greater Los Angeles.

Katrina, on the other hand, destroyed more than 80 percent of New Orleans, plunging the majority of the city into a dark, lawless world. The NOPD lost hundreds of officers leaving the remaining force responsible for securing the small, populated strip and patrolling the blacked-out wastelands.

And yet somehow you think it is fair to draw a comparison between the arrest of one person in Los Angeles to overseeing a hurricane ravaged city?

Is it that simple?

More importantly, are you that simple?

Again, do you put any thought into your columns or do you scribble them on a bar napkin before the bouncer throws your bloated ass out on the street for trying to stick your dog-popsicle dick into the hand-dry machine?

Damn, where's my therapist when I need her?

You go on to say that Nagin needs to "jack up some teenagers with guns." What in the hell does that mean? Do you mean he should send the cops out to pound their heads into the pavement, these "teenagers with guns?" Should the cops do random house searches, bashing down doors looking for these "teenagers with guns?"

At this point you'll get all albino-macho and say, "Hell yes! Knock down doors and teach these kids a lesson!"

Good advice if we weren't living in a country with laws. Good advice to advocate the use of extralegal methods when certain members of our police force have a notorious history of abusing and terrorizing the citizenry.

But that's the Daryl Gates way, right?

That's the Fox News way--pale, flabby men, your nipples raw from rubbing pictures of Abu Ghraib on your areolas, trying to out-man each other by talking big on camera. But when the lights go out you're in some Reno whorehouse dressed like a soldier paying some 19-year-old tramp to call you Patton.

You next ask a question so absurd I'm loathe to repeat it. But here goes....

"Troops are for Iraq. The cops should be able to handle New Orleans. And you wonder why Nagin and his cops don't? Have they decided the city does belong to the street gangs?"

I don't know. Just because Iraq is a cauldron of unabated violence does it mean that the U.S. Army has decided the streets of Baghdad belong to the insurgents?

Is the inability of a tortured and damaged police force to control a Baghdad-like environment an indication that they have conceded defeat?

You simpering cow.

The cops are hurting. Our people are being slaughtered. We need help. Yet when we ask for help you tell us to go fuck ourselves, that only the people of Iraq deserve the assistance of our armed forces. But we're not surprised. I get your agenda. Katrina has been a black mark on the record of your Pimp-in-Chief and you can't stand that.

Better to deny that this was a once in a lifetime historic event. Treat it like just another city filled with welfare queens and uncontrollable darkies, run by soft-on-crime liberals who simply aren't up for the job.

You follow that slice of idiocy with this--"Since when do cops need troops as backup for kids with guns?"

First off, you continually refer to these insanely violent murderers as either "kids" or "teenagers with guns" as if to diminish their lethality.

Of course, if you were in charge, big tough John Gibson, you would rummage through your rum closet and get out your trusty two-by-four and teach those rascally kids a lesson. You'd take them by the scruff of their necks, throw them over your knee and get to paddling.

These silly kids with guns.

But let me take a quick moment to tell you "since when" cops need help from the troops. Since Katrina demolished our entire city.

Since a large percentage of our police force has been forced to patrol deserted neighborhoods to protect vacant homes from looters.

Since our city has been overrun with bloodthirsty teens with submachine guns.

That's when you pompous, pointless waste of sperm.

You say it's a mystery why the cops haven't been able to solve our crime problem. Well, things remain a mystery to those who do not actively search out answers. But that's not your gig, is it?

Fuck the truth.

Hell, those kids at Kent State deserved what they got.

And the people who "refused" to evacuate before Katrina suffered the repercussions of their inaction.

No need to shed tears.

I never expected reason or logic from you, just misinformed, pro-conservative rants without any forethought or human compassion for people who don't share your world-view.

It's sad that you can't take a few minutes out of your devotion to the patriotic penis pump that allows you to dry hump your silk taffeta-adorned blow-up Strom Thurmond doll to find out what is really happening here.

But please, keep corrupting the airwaves with the disease of your mindless commentaries. They keep my rage in tune with my paranoia and in these post-Katrina days there's no better shield of armor.

And I like to think my therapist would have cleared this, my tempest of anger, had she had not fallen victim to the promises of a man and a charred spoon.

* * * * * * * * *

Murders rip Central City recovery bid
By Richard A. Webster New Orleans CityBusiness Staff Writer

July 14, 2006 -- After nearly five murder-free months following Hurricane Katrina, an unknown assailant gunned down 20-year old Derrick Brown at 2229 Magnolia St.
The next day a hail of bullets claimed 37-year-old Corey Mitchell.
In the next five months, gunfire murdered 13 more people, culminating in the massacre of five young men under the age of 20 at the intersection of Daneel and Josephine streets. The common thread tying these 15 victims together is the location where they met their ends — Central City.
Prior to Katrina, Central City in the Sixth District was not immune to revenge slayings and bloodletting. But it was overshadowed by the more notorious killing fields of the Lower Ninth Ward.
After Katrina obliterated the Ninth Ward, the tide of violence shifted to Central City as ground zero for New Orleans to once again become the Murder Capital of the United States.
What is it about this neighborhood that makes it so attractive to thugs, drug dealers and children of the semi-automatic who settle the most minor of differences with the pull of a trigger?
Immediately following Katrina, New Orleanians enjoyed a city virtually free of violent crime. But after the first of the year, the FBI said the "legacy African-American street dealers" began to return.
The New Orleans they returned to, however, was nothing like the New Orleans they left, said Jim Bernazzani, FBI special agent for Louisiana. Familiar neighborhoods like the Lower Ninth Ward and the housing projects that served as safe havens and profitable drug markets were wiped out. Like so many residents returning to the city, career criminals and drug dealers had no place to live in their former homes so they turned their attention to the 20 percent of the city spared by Katrina.
For many, that meant Central City.

"In Central City there are a lot of abandoned homes and (the returning drug dealers) are squatting in these homes and they're bumping up against individuals who used to control that turf before the storm," said Bernazzani. "It's not as sophisticated as them staking claim to territory but they're definitely running into each other."

In 2004, the 29 Central City murders accounted for 11 percent of the 265 homicides in New Orleans. As of July 1 this year, the 16 Central murders accounted for 28 percent of the 57 murders citywide. Louis Harding, 72, a lifelong Central City resident, said as bad as New Orleans was for the African-American lower class before the storm, it's become even worse with the destruction and loss of so much housing.

"Central City has become more violent. But if they tear down the projects like they're talking, you ain't seen nothin' yet," Harding said. "You're gonna have a whole lot of people having nowhere to live and then you'll have a whole lot of things happening on the streets out there like we've never seen."

Before the hurricane, the 3.9-square-mile Central City neighborhood between Uptown and the Central Business District was flanked by three major housing projects — B.W. Cooper, Guste Homes and C.J. Peete — with a fourth, St. Thomas, in operation until its 2000 demolition. The area was familiar territory for the criminal element and favorable for drug dealing, said University of New Orleans criminologist Peter Scharf.

"Your most at-risk people came back here first, the people that couldn't make it in Houston," Scharf said. "This is an underclass that won't quit, an illiterate, violent underclass, a culture of kids who see murder as an interesting business strategy, and Central City has all of the characteristics of a neighborhood favorable to drug dealing. I think we fooled ourselves into thinking the hurricane could eradicate crime. We wanted it to be true more than it ever was."

Before the demolition of St. Thomas, homicides in Central City typically exceeded 100 a year. After the city razed St. Thomas, murders dropped off to 51 in 2002, 24 in 2003, 29 in 2004 and 25 in 2005 as of Aug. 29 when Katrina hit.

However, when St. Thomas was demolished, many residents relocated to projects at St. Bernard, Iberville and Lafitte. This resulted in widespread unrest and former St. Thomas residents were being marked for murder, said Capt. Bob Bardy, Sixth District commander. The same violent dynamic is playing out in Central City.

"Central City is fully populated again and in some cases you have four families living in one house," Bardy said. "We're seeing all of the same criminal names that we saw before the storm but we're also seeing people who used to live in places like Lafitte. And a lot of times the violence isn't over drugs; it's about honor, respect, over things like a card game or a girlfriend."

Al Mims Jr., 52, has lived in Central City all of his life. Since 1988 he said he has attended more than 2,000 funerals, many for children as young as 3 years old. What is happening in Central City is the same thing that would happen if someone placed a bone between two hungry pit bulls, he said.

"You got drug dealers coming back from all parts of the country into one area. That's like having a Winn-Dixie, Sav-A-Center and Wal-Mart in the same area except, instead of trying to put each other out of business, they kill each other. I'm tired of relatives calling me from California asking what in the hell is going on down here. It's not the Wild West but it's damn near that."

Bardy first served in Central City from 1996 to 2002 when he helped reduce murders 60 percent from more than 100 to 51. He then served two years in the narcotics division followed by a two-year stint in the Seventh District in eastern New Orleans, where he reduced crime 29 percent. In May, Superintendent Warren Riley asked Bardy to return the Sixth District to help quell the recent crime epidemic.

In the past two weeks, Bardy said they have reduced crime in some of the more notorious areas of Central City and have regained the trust of the community. But until widespread changes are made throughout New Orleans, violence will continue to be a way of life for many.

"(New Orleans City Councilwoman) Cynthia Hedge-Morrell said it best that we're reaping the disasters associated with an educational system that's been defunct for 30 years," Bardy said.

Katrina drastically altered New Orleans but not the obstacles that have traditionally stood in the way of law enforcement, Bernazzani said. Citizens remain reluctant to testify against suspected murderers out of fear they will beat the rap and return to the streets with a vengeance.

"When the perception in the community is that the state judiciary has failed them, the second judiciary kicks in — street justice, which leads to revenge killings. When we run our wiretaps, New Orleans is the only place in the country where gangs refer to misdemeanor murders. They know if they keep their mouths shut and the NOPD can't get the report to the DA's office in 60 days they'll walk. I've never seen anything like it."

* * * * * * * * *

So it's the Fourth of July and it's hard to make out the gunfire from the fireworks. At 5:30 p.m. I heard a flurry of blasts but never thought much of it again until two hours later when I turned on the news.

Five blocks from my temporary home three people were shot during a card game.

I ain't saying there's no hope but hope better wear a flak jacket.

And a fire-retardant onesy.

I'm expecting half the city to go up in flames tonight from the stray sparkler sparks and fireworks bursts.

It's become sadly apparent that the most likely routes to death in New Orleans are the following--bullet to head, consumed by flames, suicide or cirrhosis of the liver. But that's nothing new.

There's a pall over the city when just a few months ago, following Mardi Gras and Jazz Fest, we felt so good about ourselves, so damn lucky to be alive.

It looked like we had a chance.

But here we are between the bullet and flame and sword and hate.

I don't even trust myself. I sleep with one eye open just in case one of my hands is planning something funny with a steak knife.

Oh shit.

I think my right big toe cut off the other nine.

Jesus Christ.

Last week it gave me assurances, told me everything was A-fucking-OK. And now this.

Looks like it's the gimp wagon for me.

All knuckles and pavement knee-caps.

Ain't it a bitch. Before Katrina the only piece of me I worried about was my foul liver with its homicidal tendencies. But now I can't even trust my eyebrows. I hear their conspiratorial whisperings late at night, the bushy little bastards, looking for a way out.

But I'm gonna hold out until there's nothing left of me, until there's nothing left of New Orleans.

At least until the end of this hurricane season. But by that time I may be a limbless raft, holding aloft a family of four desperately paddling to safety.

It's the least I can do, right?

The rest of the country is content in the idea that we'll all be fine, that New Orleans got its money and, well, hell, it's America and in America it's all good.

And I'm not saying that New Orleans is doomed. We cling to hope. But that unnatural brand of loyalty that has tied so many of us to this city for far longer than we anticipated, for far longer than our bodies are capable of--all that booze and blow and misery--it is slowly being drained from our veins.

Just a few months ago the idea of leaving was an anathema. Now, it's common conversation.

Not just conversation, but a serious sentiment.

Most of my friends did ok during the storm. We didn't lose our homes, but we're beaten. I can't possibly understand the strength of those who lost everything—family, friends, houses, all worldly possessions—the people who have every right to forsake New Orleans but refuse to.

Some would call it a sickness, a reawakening death wish.

But I see it as the embodiment of love.

For me, the idea of leaving is still a far-off concept, but it is encroaching deeper inside my psyche.

Sometimes I find myself eyeing the exit as if it were a 19-year-old girl in hot pants.

And yet I stay, committed to my addiction like a junkie, other times like a disciple, but mostly as a fiercely devoted friend.

And here I am grappling with the death-bed scenario.

New Orleans is a bum and an angel and a devil and a wastrel, a genius and monster and moron and master. It is pearl-white mansions and crack houses in flames. It is song and dance and slashing knives and gats. Dark wisdom, enlightenment, cool-night brass bands and scorching summer crawfish boils for children and beer-swilling punks and writers and musicians and students and all the mixing in-between.

And all that has happened in the past 10 months, the destruction and death, rebirth and regression, the glorious moments of community, thousands of shoulders lent to neighbors to cry on, it all makes sense.

New Orleans has never truly been a part of this country. It is an island the citizens of America visit and occasionally piss on.

But it's cool.

It makes sense that this would be the first city to be destroyed and abandoned. Why not? We've never been right in the head.

But that doesn't mean we're not right.

For a country that prides itself on doing the impossible it seems all too ready to bow down and accept its limitations when it comes to the rebuilding of New Orleans.

As our monuments burn, so do our hearts and minds.

Bukowski said, in response to the rich who claimed to know the intimate depths of pain, "No one suffers like the poor."

Well, that's how we feel. No one suffers like New Orleans.

No one.

(Except the people being massacred in Darfur, and probably the Iraqis, and the Israelis and Palestinians and anyone who is homeless and people suffering from terminal diseases and midgets. To be honest, we're not doing that bad. Basically we're drunk most of the time, like when I write this screed. So yeah, whatever. Fuck you.)

FOurteen-th Entry
August 3, 2006,

Love Song
for a
Jack-O-Lantern

"WE DIE ONLY ONCE,
AND FOR SUCH A LONG TIME."
--MOLIERE

"IMAGINE THERE'S NO HEAVEN.
IMAGINE THERE'S NO HELL.
IMAGINE ALL THE PEOPLE, CHAINED
TO THE BARREL OF A GUN."
--R.A.W.

So bitch and a handbag.

We got a hurricane named Chris that seems to be creeping its way into the Gulf. I've been anxious for the next one and this is the first of the season to pose any sort of threat, distant as it may be.

The thought of repeating what we went through last year makes me sick to my stomach. There's not a chance I'll evacuate but if New Orleans is hit for a second time in one year, well, close the fucking door and turn off the lights.

We're strong and crazy but the current mindset in New Orleans is tenuous at best. I'm on the constant verge of a nervous breakdown as are the majority of my friends. People are being slaughtered in the streets every week. Just the other day a man was gunned down outside a daiquiri shop I used to live next to. More than 50 people witnessed the crime but not one has come forward to finger the assailant.

This is New Orleans, the bloodiest fucking city in the U.S. The hurricane didn't change a damn thing.

You talk you die.

So no one talks and yet people die, regardless.

We're all on the edge.

After 365 days dealing with the aftermath of the worst natural and government-sponsored disaster in the history of the U.S, the effects on our psyches have become apparent.

You drive by destruction, every day.

You read about how our levees are forever fucked, every day.

You see people wandering our streets, lost, homeless, every day.

You see the pain in the faces of the tortured every day.

Then you turn on cable news and see that they continue to show images from that wretched two-week period following Katrina, on what seems like an unending loop.

Every motherfucking day.

You force your fist through a wall and scream for blood.

You hear that word, not every day, but every hour.

Katrina.

You try to drown (Katrina) the pain with torrents of booze that breach the levees (Katrina) of your liver and kidney and soon you're spitting blood (Katrina) and yet you keep drinking because the alternative is too ugly to contemplate.

Katrina.

"We die only once and for such a long time."

--Moliere

Before the storm I had a good shot of reaching my 60s.

After the storm, after the damage I've inflicted on my organs, I'll be lucky to hit 40.

We're frantic and nervous and blind and numb.

I have termites in my veins. Not too sure what they're doing but they itch and bite and if the data flowing from my nerve endings is right, I believe the filthy fucking buggers are copulating.

I got an X-Ray at Touro Infirmary the other day to confirm my suspicions. The doctor held the plastic black sheet in his hand and slapped it against his thigh as he looked at me with a mix of concern and disgust.

"The bad news is that the termites are reproducing in your veins," he said. "The good news is that their spawn have no chance of surviving due to the high toxicity of your blood. Of course, that leads to more bad news. Your blood has become so poisonous I wouldn't be surprised if in a week or so it completely dissolves your veins."

"So what you're saying is that I have a week to live."

"No. You'll probably be shot on the way out of the hospital."

Imagine there's no heaven.

Imagine there's no hell.

Imagine all the people, chained to the barrel of a gun.

Raindrops on roses and whiskers on kittens,

Bright sulfuric flashes and bullets are hitting

Innocent children now angels with wings

These are a few of my favorite things

Black mood all around, baby. We got misery and we got pain. But fuck it, right?

Armageddon in the Middle East.

What's a little pain in the Gulf Coast?

Who do you turn to when it all goes wrong?

God? Allah? Buddha?

How about Pablo Escobar, Phillip Morris and Anheuser Busch. The holy trinity of New Orleans.

Strange times indeed. Attorney General Charles Foti charged two nurses and a female doctor from Memorial Baptist Hospital with homicide, for allegedly killing patients, intentionally, during those wretched days following Katrina. And the public is righteously up in arms, but not at the medical staff.

192

Their ire is focused on that craven fucker Foti.

How dare the attorney general throw blame and accusations down on the heads of women who dedicated their lives towards helping the helpless. They were abandoned, forced to care for hundreds of suffering patients while the city descended into armed madness.

But political positioning feels like a mother's tit to the nervously elected.

Let the whores fry.

We gots to git dem votes.

Poppa Foti needs a brand new colostomy bag and a baggie o ' Viagra.

It makes sense to the soulless and sounds logical to the fearless, i.e. the dogs of August who stab babies for pacifiers.

I suppose if I were up for reelection I'd feel the need to throw a chokehold on a baby panda while one of my lackeys slips on the brass knuckles and lays into the soft Oreo stomach of its momma.

But I chose a different route. I chose to go all Leaving Las Vegas. I no longer eat save for two peanut butter and jelly sandwiches in the morning. You may frown and curse this life-choice but it sounds reasonable from where I sit.

There are no thrones here in New Orleans. We got two choices--electric chair or barstool. My creative mind has combined the two into a perfect amalgamation of excess and death. And you ain't never had a high like throwing back a shot of tequila as 2,000 volts of electricity impregnate your every organ.

But my personal life is my own so keep your fucking noses out of my business. I'm here to talk about hope.

There is none.

Next topic.

Happiness.

It ends when you wake up.

Mental instability.

Ahhh, now here we have a topic I can wrap my trembling hands around. Many of our traffic lights remain inoperable. At those intersections plagued by flashing red lights, cops lie in wait for someone to slip up. Yesterday, after a long night spent in the bar-world, as I drove to work, blasting the Streets album, "A Grand Don't Come for Free," I mindlessly blew through one of these flashing reds. A female officer pulled me over and asked for registration and insurance. I had my registration but no insurance. So I put on a big show, digging through my backseat for my imaginary Geico insurance card.

"Where is that damn insurance?" I shouted.

Ten minutes into my false search I threw my hands in the air and said, "I can't find it. Just write me the ticket."

The officer said if I didn't have insurance she would have to take my truck.

I resumed my faux search with much grunting and tossing around of garbage until she said she was going to give me a break.

Had I not been half-drunk and numb from what is now an 11-month bender I wouldn't have been able to pull off my wild-eyed performance that mixed exasperation with storm weary desperation.

I think the turning point came when I handed her my registration. The papers were crusted together. As she attempted to pry them apart I said, "That's from Katrina. My truck flooded."

But that wasn't true. My registration documents got wet after I left the window of my truck open one rainy, drunken night.

This is the prize of my newfound insanity--calm, cool and recklessly confident because I really don't give a shit anymore.

I'm not at the end of my rope because we no longer have any rope. We've exhausted our supply during private suicide hanging ceremonies as the brass bands hooted Taps with tubas and rolling saxophones.

So if you ever come to New Orleans, don't look up. The rafters are thick with swinging bodies, flesh chimes that make no noise when the wind strikes their soft exteriors, save for the inaudible screams of the dead.

Katrina.

Katrina.

Katrina.

365 goddamn days.

And with Hurricane Chris moving towards the Gulf, we may need to reorder 12 tons of industrial strength rope.

The dread has resurfaced.

Not again Oh Lord. Please, not again.

But whatever happens, I'm not going anywhere. I'm staying even if we get hit again. And there is a general feeling, a certainty that we will get hit again.

We live on a diet of fatalism and self-torture.

I don't have a gun but I have been assured a room at the downtown Sheraton where the national media will be camped out, eager for another round of Big Easy tragedy.

So let's either get this thing finished or try and get this thing solved.

This is a city on the eve of destruction, near extinction, and if it goes down, I'm going down with it.

The perfect end to a mad life.

I don't expect anyone to understand this attitude.

I don't expect anything anymore.

I caught a firefly with my mouth the other day. My name is Jack-O-Lantern and I sit on the front stoop smiling for the parentless children hop-scotching on broken glass sidewalks.

Two boys point at me and laugh then chase each other down the street leaving behind a 10-year-old girl. She holds a wilted daisy in her left hand, standing a foot away from me. She doesn't say a word, she just stares at me, this strange man, his mouth illuminated by the soft yellow glow of a firefly.

I smile and broken beams of light slip through my teeth.

Her eyes widen and she gasps. "Oh!"

"What are you?" she asks.

She's so innocent. And I can no longer hold my smile. The firefly dies and with it the light. I swallow the body. It tastes like rust.

I'm just a guy on a stoop, by himself, staring at a little girl.

"What are you?" she asks.

I don't know, I say.

She takes a few steps closer. Brave child. Kind girl. Full of compassion.

"You look sad," she says.

I laugh. Here is hope. Here is happiness.

"Are you a-frightened?" she asks.

I take a long, slow pull off my beer.

"No. I'm not a-frightened. I'm not anything."

She looks at me with cautious curiosity. Her nervousness is gone. There is only concern.

"You can't be nothing," she says. "You got to be something."

I got to be something.

I got to be someone.

I try to manage a strained smile but my muscles fail me.

I don't want to worry her so I say, "I am something, baby. Thanks. I'm a guy sitting on a stoop talking to the greatest little woman in New Orleans."

She gives me a shy grin and extends her hand, offering me the wilted daisy.

I take it between my thumb and forefinger. It's as good as a firefly, even better, right?

But as I'm staring at it, I feel the stem snap.

No.

I tighten my grip and watch as the blood rushes to the tips of my fingers.

I won't let this happen.

I won't let it fall to pieces at her tiny feet.

Thanks, I say.

She throws me a quick smile then races down the street after her friends.

I don't move until she disappears around the corner at Jena Street.

I wait five minutes until I'm sure she's gone. And then I loosen my grip and watch as the broken daisy drops to the ground.

I lose track of time. Dusk turns to evening. The evening gets lost in the dark.

I sit on the stoop, by myself, watching the night sky, searching for a new firefly.

Interlude
There's No Home

Tivoli evictons challenged
By Richard A. Webster New Orleans CityBusiness Staff Writer

April 3, 2006 -- Maynard Cecil "M.C." Brown, a 76-year-old Korean War veteran, lives in a van underneath the Interstate 10 overpass off St. Charles Avenue.

It wasn't always this rough for the former Marine.

Seven months ago, Brown lived in the Tivoli Place Apartments, a 166-unit, Section 8 building off Lee Circle that catered primarily to the elderly and infirm.

Brown rode out Hurricane Katrina and the ensuing weeks in the building. He said there was no damage and, other than being without electricity, it was the safest place for him, until Oct. 7 when he returned from the grocery store to find all the doors locked.

Management had boarded up the entire building, claiming Tivoli was uninhabitable and would remain so for at least a year during repairs. Residents were forced to leave without warning or formal eviction notice.

Without the apartment Brown had lived in for three years, he was out on the street with no money and no place to go.

"I don't want anybody taking care of me but I put my time in," Brown said. "It doesn't seem right. Things aren't good for me now."

Management claimed water from faucets left on by evacuated residents had flooded the building so remaining tenants had to immediately vacate the premises.

"They gave me a few minutes to gather up some belongings and the next day the building was boarded and sealed up," said Ray Menard, a 78-year old World War II veteran. "They wouldn't let us back in."

Menard eventually found a room to rent on Carondelet Street but Brown was not so lucky. Without any money or family, the Korean War veteran began living in a van under the Interstate 10 overpass.

On Aug. 31, two days after Hurricane Katrina made landfall, Dave "Lefty" Parker, manager of the Circle Bar, left his girlfriend's Uptown house to check on the condition of his music club on Lee Circle.

Parker figured he would give the Circle Bar a quick once over and return to his girl-friend's home. But as he approached he saw hundreds of elderly men and women, many pushing walkers, some in wheelchairs, wandering aimlessly in the middle of the street.

"They told me they had gotten kicked out of the Tivoli," Parker said. "They looked confused and despondent and didn't know what was going on." Brown and Menard were among the hundreds forced to leave the Tivoli. They said management ran down the hall-ways screaming that floodwaters were approaching and everyone should seek shelter at the Superdome.

After standing in the street for several hours, residents realized there was no impending flood and returned to their apartments where they stayed for the next several weeks. During that time, the National Guard kept tabs on the two veterans, at one point bringing blueberry pancakes for Brown.

Everything was slowly returning to normal until Oct. 7, when Menard was awoken by loud banging at his door. A police officer said water from faucets left turned on in several apartments was running down the hallways and management wanted the building evacu-ated. They gave him one hour to collect his possessions and get out.

Wilma Heaton, the mother of 30-year-old Clifton Bonvillian, a bipolar schizophrenic and former Tivoli resident, said she arrived at the building to check on her son's apartment just as they were kicking out Menard.

"I asked (building manager) Faye Mancuso how long I had to get Clifton's things out and she said they were sealing the building the next morning at 9 a.m.," Heaton said. "I said there was an 8 p.m. curfew and that I had 12 flights of stairs to climb to get to my son's apartment. Faye said, 'You have a problem,' and turned her back to me. These are the people supposedly caring for the old and sick? It's criminal what these people did."

The next day, management boarded up Tivoli and barred residents from re-entering to retrieve their possessions until months later.

When Menard finally gained access to his apartment in January, he found his room emp-tied and all his belongings piled on the lobby floor.

"It enrages me so what these people did to us," Menard said.

Lawler-Wood Housing, Tivoli's parent company based in Knoxville, Tenn., refused to comment on the evictions citing an ongoing lawsuit filed on behalf of the residents Oct. 27 in the U.S. District Court in the Eastern District of Louisiana.

No court date has been set.

Patricia Campbell, regional public affairs officer for HUD, said Lawler-Wood claims the hurricane inflicted $1 million in damages to the roof, elevators and windows.

When the city turned the water to the building back on in the first week of October, management claimed faucet overflows caused an additional $1 million in flood damage to the first and second floors.

Campbell said HUD investigated the claims and deemed the building uninhabitable.

"The elevators, fire alarm and sprinklers don't work and the first two floors are gutted," Campbell said. "A toxicologist deemed it unsafe to enter the property without protection and breathing apparatus."

Parker, whose business abuts the Tivoli, questions Lawler-Wood's version of the truth.

"The water in this area was never turned off and there was no one in that building except for Ray and M.C. So I'm supposed to believe that residents mysteriously showed back up and turned all of their faucets on?"

Metairie-based Citadel Builders is in charge of the hurricane-related repairs as well as renovations ordered prior to the storm.

Citadel President Denzel Clark said hurricane-related repairs will not be completed until at least the end of the year.

"When the water came back on it flooded the first and second floors from faucets overflowing. Those floors may as well have been under water. It's a mess," Clark said. "So far we've just been doing demolition and remediation on the first two floors and pre-Katrina renovations because management is still negotiating with the insurance company."

An inspector hired by attorney Jessica Hayes who is representing the residents found mold in the Tivoli but claimed it was limited and likely present before the hurricane.

"The levels weren't high enough to warrant an evacuation," said Hayes who accuses Lawler-Wood of unlawful eviction and violation of the Fair Housing Act based on discrimination since most tenants were disabled African-Americans.

Wilma Heaton, mother of a former Tivoli resident, was present during a December building inspection.

"When I arrived one of the maintenance men was wearing one of those space suits," Heaton said. "I was surprised because management had been working inside the Tivoli every day for two months without any protection and suddenly it's a dangerous health hazard? It's really a coincidence that at the same exact time the mayor allowed people back in the city for a look and leave they decide to kick everyone out of the Tivoli and shut the building down."

Gerald Andrews, 68, lived in the Tivoli for six years. He, too, is displaced like Menard and Brown.

"It ruined me when they closed it and wouldn't let us back in," Andrews said. "I can't even get in there to get my false teeth."

Andrews said Tivoli manager Faye Mancuso told him to make an appointment to retrieve his belongings and Citadel Builders would pack his possessions and bring them down to *the lobby.*

But Andrews doesn't have a home much less a place to store anything.

"They don't want us up there because we'll see there's no damage and they want us to think that it's devastated," Andrews said. "But I got into my apartment weeks after the storm and in 30 minutes I could have my place looking just as good as it did before. But you can't fight City Hall. You can't fight money when you ain't got none." Andrews has peripheral artery disease. A doctor told him it's only a matter of time before his foot will need to be amputated. He spent his $2,000 FEMA check on a wheelchair and was denied rental assistance because records show he is still a resident of Tivoli.

"I make only $609 a month on Social Security," Andrews said. "Rent at the Tivoli was $130. I can't afford to stay anywhere else. I cried when I counted out $2,000 for my wheelchair."

Andrews is not alone in his pain, said Parker.

"The first day I got back in October, M.C. walked up to me and said real low and softly, in a way that made his voice tremble, 'I'm (freaking) despondent.' What do you do when someone that strong and proud comes up to you and says something like that? It hurts and I don't know what to tell him."

Parker, who lost his Mid-City home, said he has done everything he can to care for Brown, including purchasing the $400 van so he at least has some shelter. But there are limits to what he can do.

"I don't have any money. The bar doesn't have any money and I'm still supporting other people who should be taken care of by the government," Parker said. "The point is that M.C. is a veteran who paid his dues in our society. They just threw a bunch of old and disabled people out onto the street."

Two weeks ago at 2 a.m., police threatened to impound the van Brown was living in and arrest him as a vagrant. Parker explained the situation to the police — that Brown was a former member of the military recently kicked out of his home of three years.

"They said they'd leave him alone for now but for how long I don't know," Parker said. "I really don't know what's going to happen to M.C. They already towed the last two vehicles he was sleeping in. Something like this should have never happened."

Lawler-Wood attorney Jim Bolner said an environmental consultant hired to inspect the building found water damage and other problems.

"As soon as it's cleaned up we'll let everyone back in. I don't know what the story is here," Bolner said.

Lawler-Wood officials denied having plans to turn the eight-story building into condominiums.

* * * * * * * * * *

Fifteenth ENTRY
August N9th 2006,
Heartbreak Tempest

NEW ORLEANS IS A WOMAN FOREVER OUT OF REACH.
SHE TEMPTS AND TEASES, COOING SOFT PROMISES OF ECSTASY
IN YOUR EAR, BLINDING THE BRAIN WHILE WRAPPING CHAINS
AROUND THE HEART.
"KNOCK, KNOCK."
WHO'S THERE?
"KATRINA."
KATRINA WHO?
"YOU DIE."
I DON'T GET IT.
NO ONE DOES.

Tap. Tap. Tap. Tap.

That's all I got.

An empty vessel.

There are people outside enjoying Satchmo Summer Fest and White Linen Night, throwing on their finest satins, sipping wine and pretending to be happy.

Or maybe they are happy.

Strange as it may sound, there are people who have managed to put it all behind them, people who have gone on with their lives, people who have managed to escape the wrath of the misery that has enveloped my world and the world of so many, strangers and friends alike.

These people, these grinning hyenas, they are not to be hated or lauded, they are a part of this whole thing as are the people who keep machetes in their bathroom mirrors next to the 400-count bottles of Valium.

We're built different.

Them and me.

Neither one better than the other.

Except for me.

I'm better and that makes me worse.

I've let this thing get the better of me. I've let it lead me down that alley where all those memories exist in physical form. And oh my do they relish the diamond-studded, brass knuckle uppercut to the jaw and one to the temple for the sake of reverence.

But the others, the blissful, they avoid the alley where the stagnant floodwaters lie still and the bodies float uninterrupted. They glide past the invitation. They slip past the opportunity for a look-see into the past.

Maybe they got something more on their minds.

Maybe brighter shores beckon.

Maybe it's a survival tactic or a therapeutic trick.

Or maybe the past is in the past and that's the end of it.

TV is nice.

Dinner was yummy.

Glad to meet ya.

Poppa got a brand new bag.

People laugh and I do as well. The key is to focus on one point on the wall. Find something to hope for. But be careful because it could be a shadow and the shadows show no mercy.

I found my spot on the wall, that thing that gave me momentary hope.

Needless to say, it proved to be a shadow and, like I said, it showed no mercy.

For a short time, I had hope. And it felt good.

And then it was gone. Just like that.

I had something to focus on, to take my mind off of this Mad Max existence. But I wasn't careful and let it consume me, ignoring my own advice. And when my spot on the wall vanished, I slipped back into reality. And what felt like pin pricks before now feel like steak knives in the heart.

Post-Katrina New Orleans is not a safe place for a broken heart. This monstrous fucking museum of death.

And that's it. No more. My personal life is a side note that I'd rather leave in the shadows, in the alley, in the floodwaters with the bodies. Where it belongs.

New Orleans is a woman forever out of reach. She tempts and teases and dances in the round with crystalline blue eyes that reflect your every emotion. She coos soft promises of ecstasy in your ear, blinding the brain while wrapping chains around the heart. She proclaims her love but when you return from the bar with two beers in hand, she's gone, in the corner or out the door, professing and confessing to your friends and enemies, your brothers and sisters, anybody but you. So you drink your beer. Then you drink hers. And then you order two more. And at that moment you're done. You're hers. And there ain't a goddamn thing that can be done about it. When the storm came it was like watching a lifelong love being raped, televised for all to see, your true love, trapped underneath that writhing, sweaty, hairy bulk of hatred and insanity. And all you can think of is saving her. Knight in shining armor.

How can you leave now, when she needs you the most?

You can't and I didn't, but after a year there is only so much the heart can take. Self preservation has to come into play sometime, right?

Right?

Seriously, I'm asking. How much is enough? When have you fulfilled your responsibility? How long are you supposed to hold her in your arms before you've sacrificed whatever chance you may have had at happiness?

I've reached the point where these questions need to be asked and answered. Crazy may be entertaining for a month or two but when she starts to plant roots there's no return to pleasant conversation and walks in the park.

Once that happens, say goodbye to Hollywood. Say goodbye to family and friends because they ain't gonna understand the weird change that has taken place and why you stare at the wall crying, searching for that long lost spot, for hope.

New Orleans slays me.
New Orleans has ruined me.
And that's ok.
My choice.
I chose this.
I choose to be this way.
No matter what I say.
These words
They're a play
In time.

The city's original plan to commemorate the anniversary of Katrina was to have fireworks and a comedy show. Seriously. I'm not making this up. Down here at the tail-end of the Mississippi we're known for unexpected choices. But this was too much to take.

Nagin backtracked to the sound of the laugh track and aborted the idea in a back alley as the stray cats had heart attacks.

Today is August 9. Yesterday, Tuesday, the city hit maybe the lowest point since Katrina laid her semen-stained paws on our hearts and minds.

John, a well-known and well-respected photographer has been having trouble as of late. Not only did he witness firsthand the horrors in the days immediately following the storm--the bodies and dying babies and starving men, women, girls, boys and grandparents screaming for food and water and some semblance of human compassion--he also lost his home and then his wife lost her job after which she left with his children, not permanently, but until things calmed down in the city. So as he continued to document the horror, he spent more time in the bars and took up smoking after 20 years of abstinence first inspired by the tobacco-fueled death of his father.

Or so I'm told.

"What else are you going to do in post-apocalyptic New Orleans?" he said.

What else indeed?

It's a question I've wrestled with myself and more often than not the answer comes back, "Nothing. That's exactly what you're supposed to do. Drink to quiet the voices in your head."

204

So we do and so John did.

But the voices never stopped chewing on his soul, the voices of government agencies and insurance adjusters telling him that he was fucked and that there was no financial aid coming his way, that he was never going to be able to rebuild his house or think happy thoughts in the quiet moments, those horrifying seconds of solitude that seem to stretch for god-dying days.

And I guess, as the story goes, it got too much for John to take.

Police pulled him over last night around 7 p.m. for speeding and driving erratically down an Uptown street. When they approached the car they knew immediately who he was as John was well respected by the cops for his work and bravery and ability to memorialize all those wretched moments with a sense of care and compassion.

But when they approached the car John screamed, "Shoot me! Kill me! Kill me!"

The police officers were shocked and taken aback and tried to talk him down but John was unhinged. It all got to be too much, the death and fear and uncertainty and those awful memories.

The memories.

"Kill me! Kill me!"

When he realized it was a request they just could not fulfill, John slammed his car into reverse, hit a cop and tore down St. Charles Avenue, mowing over the construction company signs lining the neutral ground until he crashed.

Again, when police approached, he repeated his plea for death. He wanted to die. He was begging for peace, a reprieve from all of this, this hell we've endured.

Realizing he was out of control, they threw the taser on him. But not even that put a stop to his desperate desire for death.

"Please kill me. Please. Shoot me."

I read the story while sitting in my cubicle on the down-side of chronic depression.

And it took everything inside of me to prevent the tears from washing my booze-lacquered skin.

Too much is too much and this was too goddamn much.

I haven't experienced anywhere near the torture that John has or the people trapped on their roofs or those who have lost homes and loved ones and all of their possessions. But in the past several months I've experienced my share of death and loss and heartbreak and separation and mental and physical breakdowns brought on by self-abuse.

My pain is minor and insignificant in the grand scheme of the storm, but it is real and as I sat in my cubicle reading about John, it all came to a head.

I read the story to the newsroom and it was met with quiet gasps.

I called James Arey, the head negotiator for the SWAT team. He arrived on the scene after the police tasered John. Arey's voice was quiet and respectful. He said how much everyone on the force respected John. How he himself was an amateur photographer and how amazed he was by John's work.

Arey said the police, out of respect, did everything they could to help him. This wasn't a criminal. This wasn't a man who set out to break laws and put people in danger. This wasn't a bad person.

This was a man, a victim of the storm, of Katrina, a person who gave everything he had to his city, jumping into a canoe with little regard for his own safety to document the pain of this place, of the dying New Orleans.

But beyond his job, his life was falling apart.

Cheryl Gerber, a freelance photographer, said John was one of the first people she saw when she returned to the city two weeks after Katrina. She said he looked bad then and proceeded to go downhill

"I thought eventually he would get a handle on it but every time I saw him he looked progressively worse."

To make matters worse, there are currently no mental health services in New Orleans. Arey said that in the pre-Katrina days when the cops picked up psych cases they had the luxury of admitting them to the crisis intervention unit at Charity Hospital where there were always beds available.

But Charity Hospital no longer exists so the police have two choices when they take the mentally unstable into custody. First, they can take them to one of the outlying hospitals that are drowning under the weight of caring for the thousands of former Charity patients. If they choose this path the person in desperate need for immediate psychiatric care will have to sit in the emergency department waiting room for up to seven hours, maybe more, before a doctor is available.

When their number is called the doctor will inspect them for physical injuries and then set them up with a temporary cot in a corner while the staff searches for an open psychiatric bed at a hospital somewhere in Louisiana. This can take days if not weeks.

The other option available to the police is jail, Orleans Parish Prison, now considered to be the largest intake center for the mentally ill in all of New Orleans.

It is our de facto psychiatric facility.

And the reality is gruesome.

A few years ago I went on a tour of the Jefferson Parish Prison and saw the holding tanks for the deranged, small rooms with glass doors. In one cell an older man paced back and forth smashing his fists into his head, screaming and mumbling. It was what I expected, the typical shit you see in movies. But in the next enclosure, a young man in his early twenties stood motionless, his face a few inches from the glass, his glassy eyes targeting some far off distant point.

There was nothing aggressive in his posture, nothing threatening or ominous. He had short, dark hair and a slight build.

Just past the holding tanks for the crazies were the cells for the trannies, separated from the general population for their own safety.

The prisoners in general population were rowdy and brutal, full of life and hatred, unlike the frozen kid in the human aquarium, the traumatized puppy in a pet store.

And you'd think the wildin' inmates in general population, screaming obscenities at the female guard assigned to give me the grand tour, would prove the more unnerving, but they did nothing for me. They were the same as the people I saw every day on the street corners.

But goddamn, that skinny white kid encased behind the glass shield, the statue with the crazed eyes, kept like a trophy, a reminder of our tenuous grasp on sanity, he proved to be a permanent stain on my memory.

He gave me nightmares long past midnight when the world had drawn its curtains. I saw flashes of him outside my bedroom window, dead eyes peering in, his blank, pale face hanging like the moon, reminding me of what is to come, my impending loss of mind.

But in OPP in these post-Katrina days, the mentally ill aren't given the luxury of gilded cages. They are tossed inside with the masses left to fend for themselves.

This is the option the police are given and this is where they placed John, for good or ill. They took him to jail.

Arey told me this is now a common occurrence. People in dire need of psychiatric services, people who are not criminals but have reached their breaking points, are left dying on the vine.

This is not an American city. This is not the first or second world. This is what it is--this is New Orleans, a place that has always been difficult to describe and digest. But now, it is something more, or less.

At times, it doesn't even meet the requirements of a civilization.

The national press has been running stories detailing the fast slide of New Orleans into a citywide mental breakdown. Typically, the national press gets it all wrong, but on this count they got it goddamn right.

And the pharmaceutical companies are all ears. They have flooded our local TV channels with commercials touting the latest in anti-depression chemical salvation.

A pale woman on a couch staring at her dirty slippers, a man sitting in the shadows of an unlit kitchen, his dead, suicidal eyes fixed on the camera, a teenager on a see-saw clutching a stuffed Humpty Dumpty doll, all so alone, all so close to the final solution.

"Are you depressed? Are you feeling lost? Do you find yourself flipping through issues of 'Guns and Ammo' even though you find the thought of shooting a deer in the ass reprehensible? When you fall asleep are you tormented by torrential rain, skin-stripping winds and crumbling levees? If so, you are not alone. These are the symptoms of depression and boy oh boy do we got the pill for you. Numb-erall! The fix-all, does-all, kills-all-feelings pill of all pills! Please note, this drug may not work in its recommended dosage for those living in New Orleans. For you poor saps we suggest you take ten times the legal limit. Side effects of over-indulgence may include tremendous profits for the makers of this drug that will be used to purchase barely legal (wink wink) hookers for the good people who brought you Numb-erall. Side effects of over-indulgence for users in New Orleans may include death but y'all are fucked anyway so really we're doing you doomed fuckers a favor."

While reading the account of John's public meltdown I couldn't help but picture myself in my truck, wrapped around the pole, electricity coursing through my body, screaming for salvation by way of the metallic, hollow rod of God.

I met a local photographer, David Rae Morris, outside the Convention Center where I was covering a summit on crime and drugs. We talked about John and Dave said after he heard what happened he immediately began to call his journalist friends to ask them how they were doing.

"Sometimes you need to stop and check yourself," he said. "Sometimes you have to ask, Am I ok?"

Sometimes too much is too much.

After a goddamn year living in the

Shit

You can't blame a poor

Sodden soul for

Giving into the

Death roll

Of it

All.

You can't blame

This poor sodden soul

For giving a long hard look

At the scars and blood-bars that

Have kept us permanently trapped underneath

These dark, oil-slick waters.

And now we long for

A second chance to

Take flight

On the debris-cleared paths towards

The light,

The goddamn, distant, promised light,

To a civilization free from the constant struggle
That has left us writhing in the blood delight
Of this oppressive, dying scenery
That we call home,
New Orleans,
The lie of the Big Easy.
But there's always mama booze to ease our night terrors and day tremors, right?
Oh glorious beer and tequila and gin.
No matter what appears in the papers of tomorrow, no matter the words that pass by these eyes, there is always the prospect of hope, right?
No.
Wrong.
But who needs hope when you got success?
Here I am, having covered the aftermath of Katrina for a full year.
The opportunity of a lifetime.
So everything worked out. I am one of a handful of journalists "lucky" enough to document every rotten, waking moment of this historic year.
Everything worked out.
Everything worked in my favor.
Sure, I'm a hollowed-out shell of a human being, riddled with mental instability and chemical disease, scraping for change to buy a six-pack to make it through the dark hours lest I go mad.
Go mad. Go mad.
But at least I have made my mark.

Knock, knock.
Who's there?
Hello?
Who's there?
Hello?
Is anybody there?

Knock, knock.
Who's there?
Katrina.
Katrina who?
You die.
I don't get it.
No one does.

These are dark turns.

These are the wrong turns.

What happened to the ones we ordered?

What happened to the ivories with the

Golden borders?

They don't live here no more.

But it's ok.

It's all right.

We're printing new brochures to properly reflect our new attractions for the mammary-mad masses.

Come to New Orleans! The French Quarter is back in action! Bourbon Street is teeming with sugar tits and sugary bits of bums and grain alcohol and 151-rum. The hotels are ready for action and the whores are primed with stilettos meant for silk sheet-traction. You think this place was the nuts before? Well momma, add one quart oil slick, three parts lingering dementia and 27 ounces of eternally embedded psychosis, and what you got is a whole new bag of tricks. The only time we sleep is when the cops knock us unconscious. The party has mutated into something new and you're all invited! So kick on your galoshes, throw on your laciest baby-doll lingerie and make your way down the great slithering Mississippi for a couple doses of mimosas and crack cocaine halitosis! New Orleans! We're better than ever!

And should you run into a downtrodden local with a vomit-mouth eager to tell long-gone tales of the dead and dying, do not treat him as you would the hustlers with their loaded dares, "I bet you I can tell where you got your shoes."

This one time, listen to what the locals say, and hear the conviction in their smoke and booze-rotted vocal chords.

"You know where I got my shoes?" he'll ask, not expecting an answer in return. "I got my shoes on my goddamn feet on the same streets where the carcasses of the Jackson family floated down from the lower Ninth Ward. These were Mr. Jackson's shoes. Took'em right off his feet. And it was tough too because they were big and swollen. But before you condemn me with cold eyes and judging juries, please know I said a prayer for the long-gone times of the long-dead New Orleans of old and one more for old Mr. Jackson and his children of tender mercy. These are our shoes now."

Hearts are dying and souls are dead.

But this is just one man's take.

If you think I'm being unduly fatalistic and nihilistic, contact the New Orleans Metropolitan Convention and Visitors Bureau for a more savory account of the events here on the ground.

All is well.

We're all happy.

We like parties and cake is nice.

We like dressing up in funny costumes.

We're hearty.

We're funny.

We're loony drunken bunnies.

We're a little crazy.

We're a little hazy.

We're open for business.

So come spend money.

Come watch us run amok.

Come and make us cum.

And copulate like ol' King Tut.

Think of it as a charitable contribution.

We need your money.

And then go home and tell your

Friends how our noses were all runny

From the mold and petroleum sediment

That has degraded our minds like meth, molly and

That rusty, brown humming rummy.

I dare you.

Come to New Orleans.

I fucking dare you.

Sixteen th
Entry
09092006,

V for Vivisection

SHE'S OUT THERE, THROWING ON THE FINEST SKINS OF THE
PEOPLE SHE SLAUGHTERED, CHECKING HER BLOOD-MAKEUP
IN THE WATERS OF LAKE PONTCHARTRAIN, PICKING HER TEETH
CLEAN WITH THE BONES, THE BONES, THE BONES OF THE LITTLE
GIRLS AND BOYS SENT TO AN EARLY REUNION WITH THEIR
MAUSOLEUM MOMMIES AND DADDIES.

It's on all of our minds, the coming anniversary of Katrina.

Remember, remember the 29th of......

It's out there, outside our windows, eating the cat you feed, and the bum you give a dollar to when the guilt is too much to take.

She's out there. Preparing herself for the curtain call, throwing on the finest skins of the people she slaughtered, checking her blood-makeup in the waters of Lake Pontchartrain, picking her teeth clean with the bones, the bones, the bones of the little girls and boys she sent to an early reunion with their mausoleum mommies and daddies.

But for some, every day is the anniversary of Katrina. A specter that haunts their every minute more than we, the whining members of Uptown could ever comprehend.

I'm writing a story about the Lower Ninth Ward, one year later. How much progress has been made? What is daily life like for the people who live there, the handful that have managed to fix their houses?

My friend Len and I were supposed to meet several women, lifelong residents, outside of Miss Tanya Harris' bombed-out house at 4 p.m. But 4 p.m. came and went and they didn't show so we figured we'd kill time walking around the ruins.

Cars consumed and spit out by God's misgivings, impacted and crumpled, busted and dusted by the side of the road, rusted corpses at the feet of relic houses, artifacts of a moment in history when doors and windows and roofs were expected home attachments, now anachronistic myths like unbridled joy.

Down there in the lower Ninth, down there where the wrath was fed its fuel directly from the hands of Mother Man and the nature of ignorance, it don't look too much different now than it did in the weeks and months immediately proceeding the storm.

Down there in the lower Ninth, if you listen real intent-like, you can hear the rumblings of the tide underneath the groan of the pick-up trucks and National Guard Hum-Vees.

Down there in the lower Ninth, if you fix your eyes on the proper blood mark, you can see desperate hands flailing out of tire-sized holes in sun-baked roofs, from Auschwitz attics.

And if you find your mark, and stand real still, motionless, close your eyes for ten seconds, and slowly lift the lids, you'll be transported back to the day we all said our goodbyes to the old New Orleans, to that day when 6-year old fingers fought for the strength to hold onto floating, face-down mommies.

You stand in that spot and all around you there ain't nothing but mean brown water. And from every direction come the screams, the screams, the screams of wild eyes pleading for salvation.

Down there in the lower Ninth Ward, it ain't nothin' but the ghosts, still drowning, still crying for something that will never come, doomed to the tortured eternity of damnation. We returned to Miss Tanya's house and still no sign of her and the ladies so I called and she said, "Oh my God, Rich I am so sorry. I completely forgot."

I told her not to worry. How could I be mad, sitting outside of her family's home, gutted and marked by the terrible absence of life, wind-swept by the screams from water-tank lungs, 365 days gone-by.

"You have nothing to apologize for," I said. "We'll meet up another day."

Len and I decided to drive to the levee. I wanted to show him the worst of the worst and there was no part of the lower Ninth worse than where the barge blasted through the rotten levee cement inviting millions of gallons of water into the homes of the working class poor.

They won't mind, she hissed to her children.

They're expecting you.

No need to knock.

They'll hear you coming. And if they're slow to open their doors to you, tear the fuckers down.

Rise to the challenge.

Len resisted coming to the Ninth for almost a year. He didn't think he could take it and I understood the feeling. The first time I took the tour, just a few months after the storm, I planned to hit the Ninth and then drive to Chalmette followed by the East. I wanted to see it all. But after a few hours in the Ninth I was done. I couldn't take any more. It felt like I had attended 900 funerals in half a day without a Guinness record to show for it, just a chemical headache, a darkened heart, and the death of whatever innocence may have remained in my 32-year-old soul.

But after months of prodding, Len gave in. We all did, eventually.

On our way to the levee we stopped so Len could take a picture of a shattered and hollowed-out church. I pulled my truck to the side of the road and parked near a beauty salon run out of a converted shotgun house.

A young black woman stopped her car in the middle of the street, rolled down her window and asked what I was doing.

"I'm press," I said. "Writing a story about the lower Ninth."

"That was my sister's beauty shop," she yelled. And then the front of her car lurched forward. Flat tire. A common occurrence when driving through the debris-ridden streets of the Ninth or anywhere in New Orleans for that matter.

"It must have been that pothole I hit," she said.

Must have been.

Her name was Tanya Lewis.

We tried to throw on her spare but due to technical malfunctions and a lack of tools Tanya was forced to call a friend for assistance. We didn't want to leave her alone in the middle of the largely deserted hood so we waited with her until help arrived.

During the next 90 minutes Tanya told us about her life in the Ninth where three generations of her family had lived. Her grandparents had first bought the house she called home in 1964, one year before Hurricane Betsy buried it and everything in the surrounding area in the black waters of the Industrial Canal.

Sure, Tanya said, they had their share of crime, just like the rest of the godforsaken city. "The young guys would be on the corner selling drugs but they wouldn't bother me because I wasn't a part of it."

The problem, Tanya said, started and ended with the family. The reason most of these kids were out on the block dealing smack and blow by the age of 12 was because their fathers were either dead, incarcerated or voluntarily absent from the lives of their endangered children. And their mothers, if they weren't working three jobs to support their children, were drugged-up, themselves the products of damaged, single-parent families. Generation after generation after generation.

"I came out here one day and the girl who lived on the corner over there," Tanya said, pointing to a house a block down the street, "her 2-year-old girl was walking down the street and it was almost dark. So I walked her back to her momma's house and said, 'Did you know your little girl was wandering down the street?' She looked at me and said, 'She knows when she's supposed to be home.' I couldn't believe what I was hearing."

Tanya was brutally honest when it came to the afflictions of the Ninth, but she loved it all the same. It was her home and she was desperate to return. Throughout the city FEMA has provided thousands of trailers to residents whose houses have been destroyed. And these homeowners park the trailers in their driveways and live in them while they work on their houses long into the night.

It is not an ideal situation but at least they are home.

But this was not a luxury afforded to the people of the lower Ninth Ward. The city has yet to restore water service to the Ninth and until water is restored FEMA says it can't approve the installation of trailers.

The water department says it is working on the problem but some believe they are not all that anxious to create a situation that allows for the reconstruction of this poor battered community.

"Ummm, we got water pipe problems so why don't y'all go to Houston and wait until we fix this situation. We have reason to believe serpents have infiltrated the infrastructure.

But we're on top of it. And you can be sure we'll alert you once this serpent problem has been properly addressed."

Until she gets a trailer to put in her driveway Tanya said she has been couch-surfing and trailer-hopping. It's not an easy life, she said, but she has no intention of leaving. Tanya said she has thought about the worst-case scenario, having to abandon the home her family has lived in for generations and either buying a new house or leaving New Orleans for good. But Tanya said she will do everything in her power to stay and preserve her family legacy.

"My sister, that was her beauty salon," she said, pointing to the house close to where I had parked my truck. "I would sometimes sell clothes out of there."

Tanya smiled as she looked at the broken shell of what in her mind was still a warm memory. To me it looked like one of the thousands of demolition-ready houses of the doomed. But the more she talked, the easier it became to hear the happiness in her voice and see what she saw. And through her eyes, I developed a sixth sense, the storm sense, a past tense that boarded up the holes, repainted the exterior, fortified the foundation, replanted flowers, hung a welcome sign on the front door and returned it to a time when children ran in circles of laughter while the adults danced and drank.

I see it Tanya.

I see it.

Just like you do.

"After parties, we would all come here and have the after parties." Tanya laughed. "In the back there we would barbecue and the entire neighborhood would come out. Man we had some great times."

"Is it ever not weird when you come back?"

Her smile faded. "No."

After a few seconds of mournful silence Tanya bounced back to life with the memories of what was. "People always say the Ninth was nothing but a bunch of poor people and drug dealers but it was really a working class community. We didn't have no projects here. This is all residential. All my family lived here. That's how it was. This was a family neighborhood. Whenever they start to say something about the Ninth on the news I turn the TV off. It makes me sick what they say about us."

Tanya evacuated to Arlington before the storm. I asked her how she found out that the Lower Ninth was flooded.

"One of my friends called me," she said. "He lived right by the levee. He said he was in his attic and I said, 'No you're not. Stop joking.' But he didn't sound right. He was scared and he said he was in his attic and the water was rising. Then I heard something loud and he said that the water was rising and that he had to get out somehow and jump to the roof on the house next door. And then the phone went dead. That's how I first found out."

Over the next several hours on that evil day, a long roster of friends and family in the lower Ninth made similar calls to Tanya, all trapped, all dying and dazed. She said she sat helpless, terrorized in Arlington listening to their horrified voices, their long-distance cries for help.

One of Tanya's friends died along with her two nieces. Those were the first deaths she mentioned. But that's not where her trail of tears ended. Anyone who lived in the Ninth, their list of departed friends and family members who succumbed to the darkness reads like a war memorial.

Dead children.

Dead babies.

Dead parents and dead cousins.

Dead Aunties and Uncles and high school sweethearts.

Dead grandparents and dead friends, the people they shared the most intimate and high-rolling times their lives had to offer. And death didn't stop at the water's edge. "Miss Martha lived in that house on the corner," Tanya said. "She was real old and real sick. Before the storm she started to lose it. One day she came out on her porch and said that President Bush was inside and he was having dinner with her. She evacuated but died soon after. She was sick but I think it was the stress of everything that pushed her over." Miss Martha's house was all that was left of the woman who once called it home in better days--a deformed structure, warped and lifeless. An empty porch.

Across the street from Miss Martha's house was a small single shotgun positioned in a diagonal on a lot of overgrown weeds. Tanya said it floated from its original location three blocks down and one up.

"I have no idea where those two houses floated from," she said, pointing to a two-story structure on an adjacent lot that was actually two individual houses, one on top of the other. I asked Tanya where the rest of her family was and she said some were in trailers in various parts of the city while others, like her sister, weren't coming back, at least not in the immediate future.

"It's easier for me because I don't have kids. If you do have kids you really shouldn't come back. Right now New Orleans isn't a safe place for children."

When Tanya evacuated to Arlington her uncle in Houston told her that she could stay with him.

"I told him there was no way I was moving to Houston," she said. "I told him that's where all 'those people' are going to."

Her Uncle didn't like those words. "Those people." He told her it was offensive and rude and what in the hell did she mean by "those people?"

"Those people" were her people, he said.

"I knew who was going to Houston," Tanya said. "And I told him, 'Just you wait. You'll see what I'm talking about.'"

And sure enough, a few months later, Tanya said he called and said, "How did you know what was going to happen?"

What happened was drugs and shootings and murder, death and mayhem, New Orleans-style. Tanya knew. She lived with it. And yet here she was, back in New Orleans, in the lower Ninth, desperate to return to her home.

One block away from where we stood a pack of roosters scampered, hopped and clucked through an intersection.

In the middle of this devastation and death-memories, the roosters flourished and played.

"They used to fight them down the street," Tanya said. "We even had a neighbor with a pig. He used to walk it around the neighborhood. My friends from New Orleans East said coming to the Ninth Ward, once you crossed that bridge, was like going to the country. 'You got some real hillbilly motherfuckers in the Ninth,' they used to say to me."

Tanya laughed.

And then she stopped.

It was the memory of her friends, the ones from New Orleans East, which was hit nearly as bad as the Ninth.

"I don't know what happened to them," she said.

Eventually, the people Tanya called to help with her flat arrived. Our time together had come to an end.

One of the friends was the son of Michael Knight, a legend of the Ninth Ward. He stayed through the storm. Never left. He got his boat and saved hundreds. When everyone was gone he fished off the bridge and began the long process of rebuilding. Knight is one of a handful of pioneers living in the most devastated section of what now passes as New Orleans.

His son, while putting on the spare, said something I've heard from everyone I've ever talked to from the Lower Ninth.

"They blew them levees," he said. "The people who were here all told me they heard three loud explosions. Boom, boom, boom. And then the water came."

His friend nodded his head in agreement, as did Tanya.

They blew the levees, they all said, like they did in 1927, which has been proven and admitted, and like many believe happened during Betsy in 1965.

You may shake your head. You may dismiss it as the paranoid delusions of the poor and black. You may laugh, you may snort, you may scoff, you may feel pity, and you may even feel a taste of hatred. But you must understand.

Is it so hard to believe that these people who have been ignored and shit on their entire lives, who know for a fact the levees were blown in 1927 and whose grandparents told them for a fact the levees were blown in 1965, would believe the same would happen to them in 2005?

You try living your entire life feeling like a disposable entity in the eyes of the government.

You try living your entire life watching that side flourish and laugh while yours exists in silent pride and quiet desperation.

"Why do you think we don't even have water yet?" Tanya asked. "This is the only part of the city without water. Why the hell do you think that is? They want this land for themselves. They always have."

This is how they feel.

This is what they know.

There was no doubt in their eyes.

And I don't question them.

Their sincerity.

With the spare on the car it was time to go. We shook hands and said goodbye.

To these three residents of the Lower Ninth Ward,

Who refuse to leave,

Who believe in what was and what they want to be again.

No matter what.

No matter what the pundits and papers and politicians say.

You fools, they call them.

You ready-made victims.

Suicide addicts.

Ignorant blacks.

You're standing in our way.

Just go.

Go back to Houston or Atlanta or the predestined grave.

Please. Please go and never come the fuck back.

You're a human headache.

A reminder of our failings.

Why can't you get it?

That you're no longer wanted.

You and your precious little Ninth Ward community.

Of crack-a-lack slangers and teenage baby farms.

But these three,

These three survivors,

They refuse.

They who suffered the most,

Lost the most,
Died the most,
They aren't going anywhere.
They are home and fuck you.
Kindly.
It doesn't matter what you think.
And to me,
I stand humbled.

I told you this story because I wanted to show that hope actually does exist in New Orleans, despite what I've recently written as I descend into madness and misery.
The people I met that day in the lower Ninth Ward, they are New Orleans. Those on the outside and many on the inside say, "You can't rebuild the Ninth Ward. It stands in the way of progress. Tell them they can't rebuild. It's for their own good. We're just looking out for their best interests."
The people who say this don't have the nuts to say it to the faces of those I met in the Ninth, on that dusty road.
Best to keep your distance while you drive the knife through the spine in search of the soul's weakest point.
Best to wear the blindfold while you torch the crib.
Best to maintain your postured dignity while robbing thousands of theirs.
These black children, they say.
These poor infantilized adults who do not have the capacity to see the big picture,
What's best for them.
So they must be saved. From themselves.
Before they have the chance to
Reestablish all that ugliness,
The stain on our tender sensibilities,
The land of pestilence
Where shell-casings rained on
Blow-covered sidewalks
Trampled on by the
Chalk-outlined souls of
Who gives a shit?

Seventeen(17)th Entry
Sept. Sixth Two006,

THE LAST KISS:
ONE DEAD YEAR

YOU SHOULD TRY IT SOMETIME, A VACATION IN THE STRAPS
AND BUCKLES, A SOJOURN INTO THE WHITE WALLS OF
QUICK-ACTION NEEDLE MARKS YOU NEVER SAW COMING.
IT TOOK A LONG TIME TO HAPPEN, BUT IT HAPPENED AND
SO BE IT.

SO IT GOES.

The New Orleans summer--it's hot, a dead heat that clings to you, draped over your shoulders, a shroud of sewage and swamp water, a second skin of melting flesh and bones. First you take off your shirt, then your pants and socks and shoes. If you got a beard you shave it. If you got hair you damn it. If you got a beer you drink it.

It's the eve of Katrina's birth, Aug. 28, 2006. There's a sick, uneasy feeling throughout the city as media outlets descend to prod our psyches and stir the water-corpses with microphones and flash bulbs.

"Wake up and prove you really died," they demand of the dead.

And to the living, "Lie down and prove you're not already dead, because we ain't be-lievin' the shit you been tellin' us. Where's all the progress and momentum? What you been doin' down here? From our vantage point it looks like it's been nuthin' but a whole lotta drinkin' and fuckin'. We demand answers and receipts for our kindness."

One year later.

At times it feels like a month.

Other times, it feels like a lifetime.

And if this is Buddha's idea of reincarnation, the fat bastard can suck on the tailpipe of my Bronco and get down with the deep-cough skeleton dance.

I'm not really sure why I wrote that.

Or what it means.

I'm sitting on the second-story enclosed porch of my temporary new home. Moved in three weeks ago, will move out in four. My friend, Kimble, was kind enough to put me up when my last place of residence fell through. He's moving into a house he purchased at the end of September and said I can live there through the end of the year while I search for affordable digs. Once I find an apartment I will have had five homes since Katrina made landfall.

Five fucking homes.

But I got it easy.

Most don't have a home. 300,000 people remain evacuees and they're suffering and dy-ing, particularly those mired in Houston where they're treated like cancer.

One year later.

Damn, I should be rolling out some strange demented wordplay but I don't have it in me. You figure upon the eve of the anniversary I would be inspired but I'm just tired and beaten.

Living here full-time since the hurricane is a personal and public psychosis.

You search for moments of peace and happiness but the tricky little fuckers hide in the dark corners. You chase them into the oil pits only to discover they were neither peace nor happiness, after all, but lies meant to temporarily placate and soothe.

And so you emerge like an inky beast and trudge home leaving behind a trail of personal failure and humiliation. And that ain't no way to live.

You need something to fight for and in the beginning we all had that fight in us. It was us against the world. Now it's just us crumbling under months piled upon months of stress and slow-creeping inebriation and undulating memories of days spent in limbo with not a hell of a lot to show for it.

But goddammit we tried.
We tried.

At first we were happy to be back. Ecstatic. The city sparked with an unheard of energy of a returning force of hope and love. We were going to show the world how badass we all are. And in the end, we still may.

We might.

But on this evil eve of the anniversary of all this destruction, it's hard to raise our glasses for anything but selfish self-medication.

It's not defeat. I'm not there yet and don't believe I will ever be there. I haven't plowed through 365 days of absolute emotional and physical hell to give up on my adopted home, where I will be buried, most likely before the age of 40.

My commitment is real, but so is that sound outside the walls of this house, thousands of spider-thin limbs swarming the plaster and tapping on the windows. It's not paranoia. It's not the oncoming signs of a soon-to-come intervention or an institutionalized commit-ment. It's just something that is a constant nowadays, a presence, a feeling of madness in the rearview mirror.

So tomorrow, on the anniversary, there will be marches from the lower Ninth to Congo Square and two jazz funerals and prayer services and vigils. There will be some who gather together with friends at private residences and others who get loose in bars with bottle-rows and powder lines.

And there will be those who choose to go it alone, in darkened rooms with faces in trembling hands to catch and smear those ever-present tears against worn skin, tormented by the memories that refuse to leave them be, no matter how hard they pray or how deep they drink or how long they inhale, be it in the waking daytime or nightmarish night or in the damned hours before dawn, those memories are forever.

They are now a part of our DNA, those rotten tears.

And there ain't a damn thing we can do about it.

365 days.

We all know people who have left our lives, be they the living or dead. And for as long as we choose to remain in this bloodletting corpse, we will never escape what happened.

And I suppose what matters is what we choose to do in the ensuing years.

I don't blame myself for losing my shit in the immediate year of the aftermath.

And make no mistake, I have lost my shit.

It took a long time to happen, but it happened and so be it.

So it goes.

You should try it sometime, a vacation in the straps and buckles, a sojourn into the white walls of quick-action needle marks you never saw coming.

Some have followed this path of mine, others have reverted to a zombie-like state, while a small unfathomable population has carried on with smiles, embracing daily chores and happy dinners, displaying either an impressive show of strength or an even more impressive dedication to denial.

"Hey man, you wanna hit the Quarter and freak some hoes?"

"Ummm, no. I've gone crazy."

"Your loss man. Boozy-bluesy tits and ass."

"Ok. Yeah. I'll go. Just give me a second while I clean my gun with my tongue."

I'm tired of recounting the current state of the city, the statistics and particulars. You want some specifics? Search them out yourselves. They're everywhere. Google the motherfuckers. I'm done. If you don't understand the full scope of what has happened, especially after reading all that I have written, then you never will.

If you insist on condemning New Orleans and myself for feeling the way we do, for taking this apocalypse as hard as we have, for not living up to preconceived expectations of strength and resilience, this has all been pointless.

I'm not asking for sympathy. None of us are. All we want is understanding, a conscious effort from the people who do not live in New Orleans to seek out information on your own, to listen to the people here on the ground, the only ones who know what the fuck is happening.

224

And if you think we're weak, you're sadly mistaken. We have persevered in a city that has devolved into a never-ending wake, an eternal funeral march.

I brush my teeth with ash.

I wash my hair with sulfur.

There are thousands of people throughout New Orleans who have donated blood to the hundreds of nails and shards of broken glass that stand in the way of repaired homes and resurrected families. They are defiant and pissed-off and consumed with a tunnel vision for the old days when the problems of life didn't seem so cataclysmic.

That's why we've stayed, every single person I know who has endured this past misery-dominated year.

We are survivors, badly broken but breathing nonetheless. One year.

365 days.

There are those who have left and those who have died and others who taken their own lives.

There are those who are on their way out. It's only a matter of time. They speak of it in hushed tones, in quiet moments, when no one is looking, only to the best of friends.

But the idea of leaving for the remaining is a breach of faith, one not to be undertaken lightly.

It is a betrayal.

But for most--though we may be hanging on by fingernails, embedded in the rotten banks of the Mississippi where the lost bodies forgotten by the U.S. Census Bureau drift like unmoored rafts, searching for purchase--there is a constant reminder of what has been lost, the forgotten myth of the resurrection. These haunted human logs, all of these untold stories, hundreds teeming the River, thousands clogging the pathways of the barges that speak of a centuries-old city, revered and reviled in the same breath, revoked and rejoiced and quietly resented, it is to them that we dedicate every day's new breath, it is to them who we owe everything.

Our private dirges.

Remembrances to be embraced.

Don't forget.

Don't deny.

365 days.

When I first started this opus, my attitude was that we were on our own. And one year later, damned if I wasn't right.

We are on our own, despite the flood of volunteers and international good will.

We are on our own because that's just the way it goes when you find yourself living at the tortured end of oblivion.

So sleep well and
Kiss angel children goodnight
While wishing them the dreams of
Kings and queens.
Gently kiss the unblemished cheeks of the
Hopes of tomorrow.
All the peace and wisdom,
All the joy and happiness fools can imagine.
Set them free with love and
Allow them to embrace the untold future.
We neither bear nor harbor ill will,
Despite my sometimes acid-words
And devilish ambitions.
I am not a victim though at times
I wrap my bony shoulders
In the robes of martyrs.
I'm just a dumb motherfucker with a love of booze
That sometimes gets the best of him.
A romantic fool with a mean streak and a
Vicious impatience for indifference.
A guy who happened to fall in love with a city
And her people
Who have witnessed something
Beyond words or
Prayers or
Nightmares.

At times my perspective has been jarred loose by
My unflinching rage.
At times my rage has been jarred loose by
My growing depression.
And at times my depression has been jarred loose by
Noble souls determined to survive,
Despite the stains on their minds,
Born from the shrieks that rifled through the hot fog of that

Goddamn day,
From the attics
Where couples and
Families and the
Loneliest of all people
Struggled and
Cursed and
Wept and,
Finally,
Made peace with
The end,
As they helplessly watched the Water rise,
And shuddered,
Questioning their sanity,
Upon hearing the creeping darkness whisper,
"I'm coming. I'm coming."

This ain't no eulogy,
Though at times it seems like one,
In the early morning hours,
When a tired body
Hits the bed in drunken exhaustion,
With nothing to show for anything
Except another brick in an
Ever-growing fortress of
Secretive suicide.
And I am close to crafting my own.

One year.
365 days.

But now isn't the time for eulogies or elegies or quiet moments of despair, though they
are indelible in our existence down here, at the end of the Mississippi.
As the infancy of America played out, cities popped up along the mighty River. And
though they are all touched by her tender banks, there is only one that is truly loved by
the great current, only one that is held in blessed regard above all others.
New Orleans is that offspring, that wild child, swinging whiskey bottles at passing stars,
laid out in fields of jasmine, naked, laughing for fools and the benefit of her enemies.

Fearless and tortured. Pure and corrupted with acid abandon.

Anybody who ever spent any significant amount of time wrapped in her pre-storm charms knows that death and personal destruction was always a persistent possibility that we wore with an even mix of dread and ill-conceived pride.

But we were never blind to the dangers of our addiction. The recent wave of evacuees, though the largest in our history, wasn't a new phenomenon. Evacuation has always been a part of the plan for most ex-pats who arrived in New Orleans--stay for a year or two then run screaming for the safety of America. It's a perfectly sane option and I never faulted my friends for choosing door number three. Most who did so are healthier and more in touch with their inner sanity and outer well-being.

Why stay in New Orleans?

This doomed terrestrial planet of alcoholism and lost dreams.

"I'm going to do something great," the drunk said to me in my first few weeks in town. "I got an idea for a book and in a year I'm going to be a goddamn legend." I smiled and patted the noble fucker on the back and said, "Hell yeah man. Me too. This is where we feast on inspiration."

Nine years later that same sad drunk sits at the end of the bar saying the same damn things. His once slender nose cratered and inflated, his limbs atrophied, his skin pock-marked with sin.

"What happened man?"

He says nothing, but if you watch closely, you can see a slight movement of the neck that is meant to result in a back and forth motion of the head. A signal of recognition. But it's all inertia now.

"Nuthin' mans. I gots the ideas in the works but you know hows it is. You know? God-damn New Orleansh. Goddamn."

And then came the great tide that swept all of us off our bar stools, washing the brightest and drunkest into the River and few resurfaced.

Few returned.

But for those of us with the foresight to craft snorkels out of bottomless beer bottles, we are back and flush with something, whether you want to call it madness or insanity or 12-pronged clarity, we believe it will result in salvation.

The point is we are back and in spite of my nightly raid on the emergency supply of booze and suicide pills stockpiled in the event of the Rapture, we are mere seconds from action. Just give us some time to get it together.

Trust us.

That's all we ask.

Just a few seconds.

To catch our breath.

228

To come to terms with what's left
In the medicine cabinet.
Give me a moment.
One precious moment.
And I promise,
When I open my eyes,
You'll see a new man.
One year.
365 days.

A lifetime to go.

"Just a prayer for New Orleans
Please don't stare
I'm from New Orleans
Just a prayer for New Orleans."

--Charlie Miller

--matosantos r.a.w.

Year one: end

Epilogue: Year One
sePTembeR 12, 2006,

R.A.W.

in exile

DON'T WORRY DARLIN'.
I PROMISE.
IT'S JUST SLEEPING.
HAD A LITTLE TOO MUCH TO DRINK.
JUST LIKE ME.
BUT TOMORROW,
GODDAMN,
WE'LL ALL HEAR THE SONG,
EVEN IF IT MEANS
WE'RE ALL A LITTLE CRAZY.

AND SOMETIMES,
THAT'S WHAT IT TAKES.
SOMETIMES,
THAT'S ENOUGH.

Naw maw, I ain't leavin' the city or callin' it quits with bits o' buckshot to the head.
But with the summer comin' on down to a close and ex-sportscasters dressing like bums
and shootin' their wifeys in the nose, I figure it best to retreat into the shadows.

There were 14 shootings over Labor Day weekend. One guy had shot the same victim
just a week earlier. He turned himself in, the judge set bail at $30,000, the alleged shooter
posted bond, hit the streets, found the mark he failed to kill before and shot him again.
Police arrested him once more for the same crime against the same guy. The judge set the
bond for over $100,000 and back in jail the would-be assassin rots.
I imagine he'll be out in 60 days for a third try.
As the days streak by and the mobile, gangbang-units gather momentum, there's not
much you can do but fear your time is nigh.
At hand.
So collect what dust you got and head for the darkness.
Not out of fear. Honestly, it's a mix of self-preservation and what I like to believe is good
public policy.
It's exile time for me, down deep into seclusion.
I'm no longer fit for mass consumption.
For them out there.
High arcing beer bottles smash on the pavement with low-crashing joy every time I leave
or enter a bar.
A weird coincidence.
At first, my paranoia led me to believe I was under attack by some holy-rolling manic
street preacher. But I fear this unusual occurrence may be the product of my own hand,
a tic developed over these past several months of concerted fire-breathing alcoholism
during which time a web of hostility, rage and depression has given me a fishnet-stocking
veneer.
I'm to blame.
I'm the fucking drunk throwing beer bottles in the air. I like to hear the smashy-smash of
the glass in the middle of the street where cops and creeps abound. I don't know why.
I'm a polar bear with a beach ball.
I think something broke in my brain some time ago.

I've also grown a fondness for punching inanimate objects and often times my own face, sometimes with scissors for the ultimate impact.

So I'm thinking it may be time to drift into the shadows. A little obscurity for a little peace of mind. Not a bad trade-off. For myself.

And them out there.

But no worries, for the sad times and mad times have not come to an end.

Please be kind enough to assure your families that New Orleans is not back to its old ways. But also be cruel enough to reassure them we've found new ways, filed by bone-knife to heighten the pleasure and panic.

Alas, it's all the same when you come down to it.

Gentilly, eastern New Orleans, Lakeview, the lower Ninth Ward, Chalmette, Slidell......
it's all fucked, fucked enough that a delegation of community activists traveled to Thailand to get tips on rebuilding from third world fishermen who suffered through the 2004 tsunami.

And when villagers from the tsunami-ravaged region toured New Orleans in June, they couldn't believe their eyes, said Brad Paul, executive director of National Policy and Advocacy Council on Homelessness in the Lower Garden District.

"They were shocked. They couldn't believe a country with so much money wouldn't have rebuilt the city," Paul said. "They were stunned by the level of devastation."

So if they're shocked, imagine how we feel, the dumb animals who have lived in this shit for the past year.

And this is what it has come down to, the people of New Orleans being openly mocked by Thai villagers, the great behemoth known as the United States held up for ridicule by third world fish-mongers.

So it has been, so it is and so it shall always be.

But we here in New Orleans don't mind absorbing a shot or two by the talented net-hurlers of Indonesia. Hell, we've always considered ourselves a third world country, if not as a source of pride than as a way to reinforce our belief that we are something apart from the rest of the country.

Only now our third world status is being forced upon us by the inaction of the federal, state and local governments.

Ahhhh, but an epilogue is no place for such recriminations.

I mean to go out on a completely deranged slant to make up for the past several entries drenched in abject despondency.

Let's not play footsies under the coffin with the demons that have forced their horns into our backsides ever since Katrina, by way of gross federal incompetence, laid waste to our taverns and tombs.

Let's not point fingers or finger the angels yet to come to our rescue.

232

Let's suck down the last remnants of this past year and look forward to something, if not better, as emotionally charged as these past 12 months.

Down here, in the brutal south, we like to feel something before we let it all go numb.

For all the car-devouring houses that came to life in the Ninth Ward last August 29,
For all the waterline fairies who painted high brown streaks on our homes,
For all the rumors of murder and mayhem
And the facts and evidence that spoke
Truth to power,
For all the apologies laid forth by the Corps of Engineers,
For our guitar-playing Nero cowboy president
With his flyover promises of hope,
For the baby-talking rap of our Governor and
The idiotic brilliance of our scat-man mayor,
We thank whatever gods may be for our unconquerable souls.
Despite our madness and sadness and
Inability to hold steady hands
As the booze and chemically-enhanced
Never-ending weeks dance through the slipstream of our blood,
We stay true to the prayer of New Orleans.

From my balcony perch I see the lights of the Crescent City Connection where the Gretna Police Department held back hundreds of New Orleans evacuees from crossing into Jefferson Parish, to safety, going so far as to fire guns in the air to turn them around. And then they turned their smoking barrels on the wheelchair-bound, the crying, starving children.

While writing an update on a lawsuit filed against the city of Gretna I called the honorable Mayor Ronnie Harris for comment.

An hour later my phone rang.

"Mr. Webster, this is Mayor Ronnie Harris."

"Thanks for giving me a call back Mayor Harris."

"Yeah, well, I wish I could say I'm happy to be talking to you," he said. "When you wrote your little story about race relations in Jefferson Parish you basically accused the entire city of Gretna of being filled with nothing but racists and I have not only a problem with what you wrote but I have a problem with you sir."

One year later, everyone remains raw, consumed with what happened back then, one year ago.

And I'm used to being hated by certain public officials such as Sheriff Marlin Gusman.

He didn't shine to a series of stories I wrote about the botched evacuation of the Orleans Parish Prison. After he threatened to sue me and the paper he showed up at our offices with two beefy, armed guards ready for action.

So I wasn't taken aback by Harris' tone. But having gone two days without drinking my nerves were frayed and I was starting to get the itch.

"I haven't had one person in the entire city of Gretna, including anyone from our African American population, say one critical thing about the actions we took that day," Harris bellowed. "We were protecting our citizens. We didn't have enough police to protect those who had stayed behind, most of whom were African Americans. We didn't have food or water and the New Orleans Police Department had no right to say that these people could storm our city. This whole thing is an urban legend."

My response can be best summed up like this: "An urban legend? Are you trying to tell me that the Gretna Police Department did not stop hundreds of people from New Orleans, most of whom were African American, from crossing the bridge to get away from the chaos and danger of New Orleans? Are you saying the police did not fire their guns into the air to scare the crowd and send them back to the nightmare of the Convention Center? Is that what you're saying to me?"

"Cars were driving fast on the bridge," Harris said. "It was dangerous for pedestrians. This was not a racial situation."

"Are you saying that you can't understand why people would believe that race had something to do with police from a majority white parish firing guns in the air to prevent hundreds of African Americans from crossing into Jefferson?"

"You're asking me to read the thoughts of people and I can't do that."

He threatened to hang up several times but I drew him back in.

"Are you saying you haven't spoken to one person, especially one African American person who had a problem with what you did?"

"Well, I spoke to one African American from New Orleans who was upset but after explaining my position he understood."

"And you think you could convince the entire black population of New Orleans that what you did was right?"

Harris closed the phone call like this.

"Well, Mr. Webster, I hope next time we talk it can be more civil."

"No sir," I said. "This was perfect."

One year later and what happened during those days after Katrina rules our lives. Nothing resolved. Rage and anger drips thick from our skin.

And as I type this, outside my window, a block down the street, three police cars have stopped traffic after pulling over two cars driven by two young black men wearing low-slung jeans and white muscle shirts.

I ain't saying it's racial, despite what Mayor Harris says about me being a racial rabble rouser.

I ain't saying these four beefy white NOPD cops have a thing against young black men in white muscle t-shirts. And I ain't saying that these young black men are two of God's sweet, candy-coated angels looking to spread candy cane wishes to the good children of the Crescent City.

I've had four 16-ounce Budweisers so my judgment may not be at its best.

This is what it is.

This is how it is, how it has always been and how it will always be.

Not much has changed from how it worked before the storm, even though 80 percent of our city is a goddamn ghost town.

The only thing that has changed is that 90 percent of the action and crime now takes place within a few blocks of the remaining fools who occupy the last livable 20 percent of the city.

We are now all witnesses.

An entire city that at any time can be called to court to provide firsthand accounts of the terror for the benefit of the terrorized, whoever they may be, whichever side they may claim.

Foolish me, I've allowed my memories to take me away from my original intent--crafting a fitting epilogue for this the first year of our new dementia, so different from the last, pure and unyielding.

Stop it.

Drink more.

I want to hear the smashy-smashy.

A Lullaby for the Lush

Oh Ma, the sights and sounds, they do creep deep under our crawling skin.

I know you wish to visit and see what exactly drew us to this mad town where your sons and daughters have lived for the past few years, to understand what keeps us tied so tight, like we once were to you and dear old Paw.

But now ain't the time.

Trust me on this one Ma.

You just ain't prepared to act as witness to sodomites swarming Sister Sally in the shadow of the St. Louis Cathedral as the junkies and gutterpunkies in Jackson Square root for one or the other to do something unnatural for the benefit of the trembling tourists clutching the black wrought iron fence, their white knuckles wrapped with cracked rosary beads that just don't seem to be doin' the trick.

"Oh God Charles, you bastard….why did you insist on coming to New Orleans?"

"Shut up Martha. Don't draw any attention to us. These people, they hear everything. They can smell our Midwestern values. It's like blood to hammerhead sharks."

"Whatever happens, just don't let them get Wendy….wait, where's Wendy? Charles you bastard! Where's Wendy?"

"She's gone. I had to give her up. A small pack of these swamp freaks came at me with what looked like whips made out of toe bones. Jesus Christ Martha, toe bones! It was her or me!"

Yeah Ma, you ain't ready to experience our wretchedly wrecked new world.

But as I said, I'm slipping back into the shadows for good measure.

It's exile time for your Irish son.

I gots to keep my cards clutched tight to my chest or else things might turn nasty, into sincere misery, damned to the House of the Rising Sun.

The myths abound but what is true is that upon Bienville settling this swamp the French government unloaded thousands of hookers and criminals onto our shores for the sake of out-populating the gators and snakes and rats and beasts deep in the weeds.

It was an economic con job.

And when our reputation for sin spread, they sent the nuns. But them nuns had no shot, no chance of quenching my forefather's prehistoric taste for flesh. And soon the nuns were selling jimson weed to the Injuns for a taste of the lash.

Sisterly bonnets bobbing under skimpy Buffalo-skin tunics.

It ain't pretty but don't think we ain't proud of this heritage.

But maybe I shouldn't speak for the entire population or even the drunks or fiends or my friends and former lovers.

Maybe I'm just speaking for myself.

Yeah. That's all I've been doing. These thoughts, though written as if universally accepted by the populace of New Orleans, they've been nothin' but crude renderings of my fragmented and damaged brain.

Maybe this ain't a public psychosis; it may just be a private descent into the mind of a masochist.

Maybe I'm the only one.

Maybe no one feels as I do.

Presumptuous drunken fuck that I am.

Maybe I've offended everyone and defended no one.

Maybe my insights are so far off the mark as to be seen as the single reason why the outside world would just as soon see another Katrina come down the pike and finish us off. That could be.

And if for some reason these lettered abdications of humanity make their way to a wider audience, maybe I will finally be forced from the place I have called home for going on nine years.

Maybe this is finally my ticket out of town.

And don't think I haven't tried to leave before.

In the summer of 1999 I fled to Costa Rica. After 20 months in New Orleans my addictions were getting the best of me. One morning I came to, splayed out on the hood of a taxi with the hands of the enraged cab driver wrapped around my throat. He was screaming something about my trying to stiff him on the fare.

Fare? I coughed as his hands loosened their grip. Fare? I just woke the fuck up with your greasy paws around my throat. Is that fair?

He tossed me onto the lawn in front of the house I shared with my girlfriend and roommate.

"Give me my goddamn money!"

I thought we were talking about what's fair? Now you're howling about money? What's fair about that?

"You owe me $22!"

For what? The pleasure of your personally meted out auto-erotic asphyxiation? That doesn't seem fair to me.

It was a Sunday and all of my neighbors were on their porches enjoying the beautiful, holy day of the Sabbath. And then this, the only white boy on the block laid out in the grass, getting a proper beat-down at the hands of a Middle Eastern hack.

As I rolled over onto my stomach I looked to my neighbor's porch. That's where my friend the cop lived. He was a kind man, a pathetic case who gave more than 30 years to the force but never rose above the level of dispatch officer. He was the first to invite me over for beers and crawfish. We had a weird bond—him, the underperforming family man and me, the overperforming lost cause. I didn't want him to see me like this and was relieved to see that he was not part of the growing audience relishing in my glorious dawn thrashing.

Jesus. What happened? How did I end up in this position?

Not that it was an unusual place for me to be.

Everything I experienced in the previous 19 months led to that point, at the mercy of the dirty boot-heel of a Turkish madman screaming obscenities and wailing on my kidneys.

Why not?

I deserved it.

I had no respect for anything or anyone.

Fuck all y'all.

That was my motto.

Young, dumb and full of evil ego.

I didn't appreciate New Orleans, not then, not the way I do now. It was nothing more than a playground for me to test every limit set before me, be it physical or moral.

Fuck all y'all.

But as I lay there in the dew-wet grass, receiving my beating, the taste of blood thick in my jowls, I figured it was time for a change of scenery, out of New Orleans, away from America.

Yeah.

This doesn't seem to be working out for me.

I woke up a day later covered in blood in my bedroom.

"I'm going out," I heard my girlfriend say.

I twisted onto my side to the crackling chorus of my broken ribs. She looked beautiful, all dressed up, but her eyes were sad, disappointed, resigned to whatever it is that I was.

"Ok," I said. "Yeah. Have fun. You go out. I may do the same. Maybe it's time for me to get out as well."

A month later, I was in Costa Rica, luxuriating in the Pacific Ocean with margarita in hand, surrounded by green-lush mountains and mono-titis and howler monkeys and fat iguanas making twisting love on the sun-oven rocks.

The perfect escape, I thought, away from all the evil influences of New Orleans. Little did I suspect that in Costa Rica everything available in New Orleans was available at a cheaper price, just a few stools down, every day and night, all for the taking.

And I took it all until it all came full circle.

One morning I found myself in the back of a cab, just like New Orleans, fat calloused hands smacking me in the face.

"Wake up! Wake up!"

What? Christ! What's your problem?

238

"You fell asleep," the Tico taxi man said. "You owe me money."

No escape. Not from myself.

Ok. Ok, I said.

I opened my wallet but it was empty.

I have to go inside my house to get some cash. Wait here.

As a sign of faith, a gesture to prove that I wasn't trying to stiff him, I gave the driver my precious orange-faced watch.

Hold this, I said. I'll be right back.

And, of course, when I returned with my cab fare, the equivalent of $5, the cabbie was gone along with my beloved watch.

Shit.

When March rolled along, after eight months in Costa Rica and no improvement in my health or behavior, I figured it was time to leave. It was Carnival season and all I could think about was getting back to New Orleans, to the parades and floats and the jazzy gris-gris sounds that first entranced me.

So I hopped the first plane back and goddamn if reentry wasn't a bitch.

Standing on the side of Magazine Street, in the middle of the mad, drunken throngs of frat boys and bloated, sweaty American bellies, I wiped a tear from my eye and whimpered, "My God, what have I done? I traded paradise for this?"

In the ensuing years I have made feeble attempts at evacuation but could never muster the strength or the will or find another city that would accept me or me it. We all try to leave and some may successfully escape for a time. But in the end we always return, as if those months we lived outside the city limits were nothing but a dream. Mostly a nightmare. This goddamn tractor beam.

Our goddamn love for New Orleans.

In spite of the bad turn my sanity has recently taken, and the downward shift that has befallen my physical health, I cannot leave, despite all the evidence that another few months in the pit will result in an eternity in the tomb.

But maybe these words will do the trick.

Maybe if a wider audience reads this, it will be my time to embrace the leper colony on the outskirts of town.

Once the general public gets a load of my roiling madness and wrong-headed conclusions, proclamations will be made on high by closet-cocaine politicians.

"This street urchin does not represent the true spirit or people of New Orleans! He must be cast out," they will sermonize through hip-bone megaphones. "He is a charlatan! A purveyor of rude, crude perversion masked as a champion of the downtrodden. But in fact he is a low-down dog, a usurper, a fake prophet with an unnatural taste for gin and the smoothy smooth legs of nubile young women. So we cast this demon out to the strange and terrible outskirts of New Orleans where the pick-up truck babies from the backwoods will deal with him in a most delicate and surgical manner."

And should the denizens of the low-lit booze caves turn on me, well then, that won't leave me with refuge or safe haven.

That will truly send a signal by way of bullet to the brain that I never belonged in the first place.

If those people, my people, don't get these words, my words, then all is lost.

But I'm betting no one will much give a shit.

You see, this here city is used to the drooling evocations of liquored-up skeletons. They occupy the highest of offices and the lowest of ditches.

And if in some crazed reality my words stir something deep in the soul of New Orleans, and if in this crazed reality what has been stirred demands my exodus, I will leave, pockets filled with bottle caps and nothing more than a smile and a sneer and the stone conviction that the many nights I spent rapping bloody knuckles on keys were a success.

For if these words offend, then truly the worm has turned and I want nothing to do with its underbelly.

All I have attempted to get across is what the cable news and print media and precious poets and quirky novelists with their clever and acceptable characters and literary tools failed to convey.

That the city of New Orleans is an open scar.

Fuck your statistics.
Fuck your demographics.
Fuck your computer graphics meant to
Graphically illustrate our progress.
Fuck your press releases and press packets
Filled with pretty pictures of smiling black bellhops
Opening doors for money-rich tourists eager to
Get their Bourbon Street jones on.

Do you know what it means to miss New Orleans?
I don't.
And never will.
New Orleans is still here and so am I.
Despite the loss of what was
We have come to accept what is,
And it smells and tastes and looks

And hurts and loves like
New Orleans.
And that's good enough for me.

It's all here,
The drunks and bums and lushes
And reckless ghetto children.
The pure of poverty and soul.
The shiny high-heeled Uptown dames and
The craggy-faced whore-romping misters.
The New York wanna-bes
Decked out in their gold-stitched jeans and tit-hugging Ed Hardy body bras
Meant to impress in the Warehouse District clubs.
The garcons and cocaine-waiters
Banging out-of-town college girls in
40-pound gumbo pots
While the kitchen crew films and gawks
And prepares blackened fillet of Decatur Street
Where musicians suck back shots of tequila
In between guitar notes and drum fills
That ice our bottles and spin us
Two seconds outside the disaster
Throwing rhythmic smiles on
Faces desperate to crack a break of joy
and return to those goddamn glorious Mardi Gras
Memories that fuel our hunger
And feed our love,
Our love,
Our untouchable love
For this motherfuckin'
Town we call home.

Save the Girl

I'm not too sure what makes this a proper epilogue. But what I am sure of is that I have spoken my peace, in search of peace, even though I have yet to find peace. And I think that's the whole point.

I don't think I've ever been after peace.

Or been at peace.

After all of this, I think that's the point.

For me at least.

And on this point I am confident I speak for myself and a small population currently occupying this relic of modern times.

Peace is fine for priests and moms and dads in search of a better life for sons and daughters and I bless them with whatever blessings remain in my corrupted soul.

For what it's worth, I say good luck and all the best.

But for me, peace is not the answer.

For me, peace of mind is death of spirit.

And in New Orleans, I have never come close to that unicorn-like peace reverently spoken of by hummingbirds around crosses and gold-plated blood flowers.

I'll take the rite of Katrina.

I'll take the passage of the storm.

And for the immediate future, I'll take my place in exile.

Naw Ma, I ain't leavin' the city or callin' it quits with bits o' buckshot to the head.

But with the summer comin' on down to a close and ex-sportscasters dressing like bums and shootin' their wifeys in the nose, I figure it best to retreat into the shadows, remove myself from the public square. This ain't my eulogy or elegy, it's just an epilogue for what was and has been.

And after many long months of mind-torture, I do believe the time has come to evaporate into the corner shadows. Despite my aversion to peace of mind, I do believe I'll wrap myself in its cousin, the warmth of isolation for a few weeks or so.

I'll allow myself a brief moment in her embrace, because I know what's to come, even though I have no idea what's going to happen.

So drift into the shadows and say goodnight Charlie.

I know it's hard but what's right is right.

Exile ain't so bad.

Love my girl.

And don't worry.

Ain't nothin' gonna change.

"Hey mister?"

I'm sitting on the stoop of my temporary post-Katrina home when a small black girl runs up to me holding something in the cup of her small hands.

"Yeah darlin'? What you got there?"

Instead of answering she slowly opens her hands. The sun shines on her prize.

I don't react much. I've been drinkin' straight going on 13 months. But I feel the need to say something, anything.

"Where'd you find that?"

"Is it dead?" she asks.

I look at the dead bird and back to her. If I tell her it's dead that makes me an asshole. But if I tell her it's not I'm a liar.

"That's a sparrow," I say.

She takes a few steps closer.

"Does it have a name?" she asks.

I put down my forty and pretend to inspect the dead sparrow for familiar characteristics.

"Yeah," I say. "I've seen that bird before."

Her face brightens.

"Its name is Jagermeister. It flew all the way from Germany. A world traveler."

"What's wrong with it?"

"Nuthin' darlin'. It's just had too much to drink. Lay it right down here beside me on this step and I'll take care of it. Go home and come back tomorrow and I promise it will be back to singing tree-songs and eating worms."

She hesitates, looks at me with intent eyes, judging my trustworthiness.

"I promise you baby, I know how to handle drunken birds. No problem. Just the other day a friend of mine had too much to drink and passed out just like that bird you got in your hand. And I took her home and the next morning she was up on her feet singing all the songs of New Orleans, like nothing happened."

"Ok," she says. The little girl lays the dead sparrow next to my forty, strokes its matted feathers and says, "I'm gonna come by and listen to it sing tomorrow. Is that ok?"

I smile. "Of course it is."

After she leaves I sit by the dead bird while I finish my beer and smoke.

It's quiet. No sirens or drunken screams or smashing bottles. Just me, my bottle and the dead bird.

Full moon. Friday night.

And though I know it doesn't make sense, I sit on that stoop for an hour, waiting for that goddamn bird to spring back to life.

Midnight comes and goes as do my friends who ridicule me for refusing the call of the craziness.

"Dump that shit in the garbage and let's hit the bars."

"I can't. I made a promise."

And they came and went and there I sat with that bird and the memory of the girl and her last words, "I'm gonna come by tomorrow and listen to it sing."

My promise.

My word.

Tomorrow.

It will sing.

Don't worry darlin'.

I promise.

It's just sleeping.

Had a little too much to drink.

Just like me.

But tomorrow,

Goddamn,

We'll all hear the song,

Even if it means

We're all a little crazy.

And sometimes,

That's what it takes.

Sometimes,

That's enough.

--matosantos r.a.w.

circa oblivion

Author Bio:

Richard A. Webster has been a journalist for 15 years, working in New Orleans, Chicago and Costa Rica. He lives in the historic New Orleans neighborhood Treme, enjoys Budweiser, lots of it, taunting the little people in the walls, electroshock therapy and starry nights. His next book, "The Nazi and the Rabbit," another collaboration with artist Sean Dietrich, will in all probability ruin his life.

Artist Bio:

Sean Dietrich is a huge, festering, untamed talent. As San Diego's top live painter, Dietrich has lashed his paint, pain and egomaniacal perspective across the faces of hundreds of helpless canvasses during more than 700 live events earning him over 70 art awards. His published works include "industriacide," "Fervor," "Mess," "Catalepsy," and the upcoming books "The Nazi and the Rabbit," "The Fruits of Our Labor," and "I Brought the Gutter," a compendium of art celebrating 10 years of Dietrich's live painting. His weird artistic and literary productions have garnered comparisons to Ralph Steadman, Tim Burton, Hunter S. Thompson and Orson Welles. Dietrich's Jameson-bred talent has infected the graphic novel, comic, gaming and film industries, laying waste to each with nihilistic abandon. When not submerged in his chamber of black ink and golden booze, Dietrich relishes in the simple pleasures of life like sliding down the edges of a glass of whiskey, drowning with abandon in the company of his girlfriend.

LaVergne, TN USA
25 September 2010
198085LV00004B/4/P